# BEASTLY INVENTIONS:

## *A Surprising Investigation into How Smart Animals Really Are*

## By JEAN GEORGE

*The Hole in the Tree*
*Snow Tracks*
*My Side of the Mountain*
*Summer of the Falcon*
*Gull Number 737*
*Hold Zero*
THIRTEEN MOON SERIES:
   *Moon of the Owls*
   *Moon of the Salamanders*
   *Moon of the Bears*
   *Moon of the Monarch Butterfly*
   *Moon of the Fox Pups*
   *Moon of the Wild Pigs*
   *Moon of the Mountain Lion*
   *Moon of the Deer*
   *Moon of the Alligator*
   *Moon of the Wolves*
   *Moon of the Winter Bird*
   *Moon of the Mole*
   *Moon of the Chickeraree*
*Spring Comes to the Ocean*
*New York*
*Coyote in Manhattan*
*Red Balloon*
*Wonderful World of Animals* (Editor)

## By JOHN and JEAN GEORGE

*Dipper of Copper Creek*
*Vulpes, the Red Fox*
*Vision, the Mink*
*Masked Prowler*
*Meph, the Pet Skunk*
*Bubo, the Great Horned Owl*

# BEASTLY INVENTIONS:

## A Surprising Investigation into How Smart Animals Really Are

### BY JEAN CRAIGHEAD GEORGE

*Illustrated by the Author*

DAVID McKAY COMPANY, INC.

New York

BEASTLY INVENTIONS:

*A Surprising Investigation into*
*How Smart Animals Really Are*

Second Printing, May 1972

Library of Congress Catalog Card Number: 72-132160

MANUFACTURED IN THE UNITED STATES OF AMERICA

VAN REES PRESS • NEW YORK

*To My Father*

Thanks for the insight into
nature and life you have given me.

## ACKNOWLEDGMENTS

My thanks to Dr. Evelyn K. Rosenberg, Ph.D., Newark College, and to Dr. Ralph S. Palmer, New York State Museum, for their consultation on this book.

# CONTENTS

The Branches or Phyla of the Animal Kingdom     viii

New Wonder Through New Eyes     1

Sculptors of Incredible Form and Feature     14

Ingenious Ways to Travel     27

Of Courtship and Sex     48

Wonderful Homes     76

Unusual Parents and Youngsters     97

Diners of Unlimited Imagination     121

Strange Worlds Through Strange Senses     143

Remarkable Deceit and Aggression     174

Inventive Ways to Live with Man     191

Principal Bibliography     209

Index     211

# The Branches or Phyla of the Animal Kingdom

Chordata (Back-boned animals)
Fishes, amphibians, reptiles, birds, mammals

Arthropoda (Joint-legged animals)
Barnacles, crabs, crayfishes, lobsters, prawns, shrimps, millipedes, spiders, scorpions, horseshoe crabs, ticks, centipedes, insects

Mollusca (Mollusks)
Clams, cuttlefish, mussels, scallops, slugs, snails, squids

Annelida (Segmented worms)
Earthworm, leeches

Echinodermata (Spiny-skinned animals)
Starfishes, sea urchins

Nematoda (Roundworms)
Nematodes

Rotifera (Wheel animals)
Rotifers

Platyhelminthes (Flatworms)
Flukes, tapeworms

Coelenterata (Sac-like animals)
Corals, jellyfishes, sea anemones

Porifera (Pore-bearing animals)
Sponges

Protozoa (Single-celled animals)
Amoeba, foraminigera, paramecium

# CHAPTER 1

# NEW WONDER THROUGH NEW EYES

THE day was every day. The towpath along the Chesapeake and Ohio Canal near my childhood home was freckled with the weeds of the Maryland countryside just as it had been the day before. The blackbirds were creaking as usual among cattails in the water by the abandoned lock, and the leaves were clattering softly as they always did. From the rocks in the Potomac River twenty feet below, the shouting between my two brothers and my father was exactly like all their shouts when they fished for the big channel cats that moved along the bottom.

Almost every day when I was eleven or twelve the four of us came to the river to canoe, fish, collect flowers, or just loll in the sun as I was doing, and I knew exactly what to expect. When the sinking sun stood on the head rock of the gorge, the men would leave the water and climb up the trail to the towpath. I would then learn another bird or plant, whether I wanted to or not, for the trio were naturalists and always came back from the river with a grabbag of insects, plants, flowers, or bird feathers, which they keyed down and identified with such enthusiasm that I would have been a stone not to learn. With the names Virginia bluebell, pepperwort, peregrine falcon, and chinquapin ringing in my head, I would yearn to be home with my cousin Ellen on our way to the movies or the store, or downtown in Washington where the excitement was.

The sun struck the head rock, the canoe beached with its familiar thud, and after the predictable interval my father leaped up the last steep slope of the embankment and greeted me. In his hand was a leaf.

"A little animal lives in here," he said. "Between the upper and lower surfaces." As he held up the leaf I could see light coming through a tiny path.

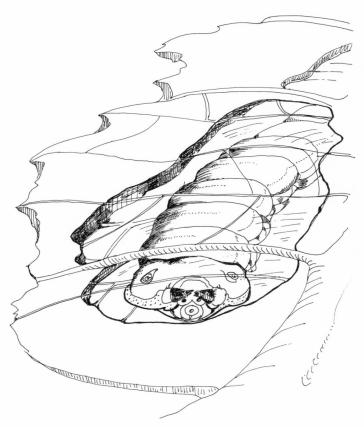

*"Something lives in a leaf?" I asked*

"Something lives in a leaf?" I asked, knowing it foolish to question a man who was an entomologist. I somehow wanted him to repeat his unbelievable statement as I took the green housing project and turned it slowly in my hand.

"The animal is legless," I heard my father say, "and is quite flat." In his informative way he added, "This particular leaf mining species, *Fenusa ulmi,* was introduced from Europe and now dwells in the Northeast and is rather rare here. It's adapted to elm leaves and nothing else. Usually it mines the English or Scotch elms, but occasionally, like this fellow, it bores into the American elm—always an *elm,* though." He opened the leaf with a small penknife, gave me his hand lens, and that day exploded into incredibility as I peered down on a greenish creature with a brown head that ate, slept, and worked inside that leaf. Glass-like windows of plant cells let in the sun as skylights do, and pale green light reflected along the corridor where *Fenusa ulmi* mined chlorophyll.

"This fellow's mother became an adult in May," my father went on, "after passing the winter in the topsoil in the pupal stage. She was a sawfly then, a creature that can identify an elm leaf—a marvelous feat when you think about it. She laid her eggs in elm leaf tissue and they hatched in about a week and the larvae began to mine inside the leaves. In June when they're full grown, they move out, drop down to the ground, and spin brown paper-like cocoons for the winter. Then they come out as sawflies in the spring—that's the cycle."

Since those days along the canal, almost nothing ever seemed usual again. I began searching around me—thinking of the leaf miner. There must be creatures in stones, roots, flower petals. I was not a scientist like my father and brothers, but without knowing it at the time, I was beginning a long search for unique animals of all kinds. It was not to be as organized a quest as theirs, but rather a hopscotch trip into worlds stretching well beyond my imagination.

Not all the strange specimens were just living in unusual

places. Leaves and sticks exhausted, I began to discover animals that travel in extraordinary ways, that build imaginative homes, or rear young as no human parent would believe possible.

For days on end I followed my three naturalists, Drs. John and Frank Craighead and Dr. F. C. Craighead, Sr., from pool to treetop in a perpetual wonder. Six years later I went off to college to study zoology and botany and haunt the labs and field camps of scientists working with every kind of animal. I assisted in a four-year field study of banded birds at the University of Michigan, and when my children came along, I explored with them and they brought whatever they found into the house. Their primers, like as not, were the illustrations and diagrams in the *Journal of Mammalogy, Nature, Science,* and obscure journals and monographs. The life histories of animals would sometimes replace their nursery tales.

Every animal, when studied, is an astonishment. They all become our folklore, but whenever I chanced on the exceptions—those that the professional biologists labeled unique —I noted and filed them.

Not long ago, while looking through my notes and assorted pages, I discovered I had a "collection." Without being quite aware of it, I had assembled an animal Hall of Fame, the Einsteins, Wright Brothers, Bohrs, Freuds, Darwins, Picassos, Romeos of the lower kingdom. This Who's Who was more than a list of the *Fenusa ulmi* of the earth; it was an unplanned testimony to animals. The genius of the so-called lower forms of life lies in their remarkable ability to adapt to every niche on earth, build "life support systems" to survive overwhelming environmental forces. Each member of my collection was specialized to cope with a problem or problems, some by developing parts of their bodies into fascinating tools, or movements into incredible actions.

Man does not seem to take his place in this strange scheme of things. A ground walker with an unusual brain, a gift of speech, and prehensible thumb, he is comparatively primitive in contrast to the specialized families. He must "think" his way back to the wisdom and ingenuity of lower animals by studying their secrets, and this is a long, unmarked trip through zoology to chemistry, biochemistry, and physics.

As in every collection, there are evasive subjects, and mine was no exception. One question was life itself, but since this is far less clear than you would think, I set out to talk to scientists of the newest and most sophisticated field, the exobiologists: men who are concerned with defining life so we can search for it in space. I approached Dr. Dale Jenkins of NASA, in Washington, D.C. Exobiology is thrilling in that it has absolute extremists on both sides of the question, "Is there any life beyond the earth?" There are those that believe there are little green men (higher forms of life, anyway) in the galaxies beyond ours, while others conclude that we are a rare and beautiful accident floating alone in the star-lit universe. In order to settle this argument, the exobiologists are trying to understand life on earth.

"The deeper we look into space for life," Jenkins said, "the closer we are looking at this planet to understand what is already here."

Years ago biologists defined life as an organism that was contained within a cell wall or membrane, grew, reproduced, had a metabolism, breathed oxygen, threw off wastes, and could not stand extreme temperatures. With exobiologists searching all corners of the earth for life, it became apparent several years ago that this definition no longer pertained. Life has been found without cell walls, in the oxygenless bottoms of lakes and rivers, in airtight fuel tanks, in the boiling pots of Yellowstone, in the ice of the Antarctic and the frozen soils of the Chilean deserts. Some of these living organisms can lie dormant for endless years without growing, reproducing, or throwing off wastes.

Furthermore, whatever life is, it is not the same today as when it began in the Archeozoic period three billion years ago, when a very different and primitive atmosphere of gases floated over the planet. Living organisms themselves help to change their gases over millenniums. Yet laboratory experiments have shown that essentially all organic building blocks of earth life can be synthesized by supplying energy to a mixture of primitive hydrogen-rich gases like those of our ancient atmosphere. When these are struck with electricity, as lightning once struck the seas, a red-brown algae appears. Although they cheer this accomplishment, zoologists continue their search. The algae-like substance does not duplicate itself, and therefore is not alive. One criterion is clear—one of the propties of life must be reproduction.

In 1959 NASA appointed a bioscience advisory group, the Kety Committee, to study the most recent data and determine among other things a definition of life, whether it had a hydrogen cycle as in earth life, or one of ammonia or silicon, or even a light cycle such as might occur in space.

They dropped from their definition of life the processes of growth, breathing, and elimination (which an organism might not display for months, even years), retaining the requirements of metabolism and reproduction. To the Kety Committee, reproduction is the means by which a "memory" or code system in living things is maintained for constant renewal. Metabolism is the fire that genetic material keeps going inside itself to get other material to work for it in its own distinctive goal of continuity. Metabolism fuels the life spark after the genetic material has succeeded in making itself a workshop of protoplasm. Since none of the three attributes could constitute life without the other two, the definition of life at this writing is an interacting formula:

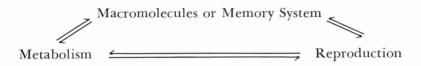

This, however, is only a definition. It is not life in the way a frog hops and birds sing. Yet it did give me insight into a code that we may never break. We are part of this thing we are searching for and must use the material of life to guide us in making our discoveries on earth and in space—an impossible task in the eyes of many biologists.

Nevertheless, with this formula scientists at the Jet Propulsion Laboratory in Pasadena, California, and the Langley Research Center, Hampton, Virginia, have designed instruments that beep in the presence of growth, of metabolism, and of the breathing of a beast. Still another gadget signals photosynthesis, the process by which plants make chlorophyll.

The instruments are strange and complex. One of them adds a spiked cocktail of radioactive broth to seemingly sterile soils. If life is there, it consumes the broth and breathes out a radioactive carbon dioxide. Next a Geiger counter moves over the spot of broth, picks up the soft radioactive breath, and beeps "life" to the scientists on earth. This instrument is a square box of wheels and gears, below which hangs the Geiger counter.

Not long ago in seemingly lifeless Death Valley, a van pulled up along the road and several scientists placed a "metabolism detector" in the hot sands. While they were returning to the truck, the gadget dug into the soil and shone a laser light into the seemingly desolate earth. The carbon dioxide which all life emits became radioactive. The receiver in the truck beeped, and the men knew life lay there beneath the hostile desert floor!

Another instrument presents a rich liver broth to the soils, some of them from the frigid Arctic. If life exists, it grows, and the clear broth becomes cloudy with living animals. Think of what messages may be sent back to us from other planets and beyond! When I expressed this to one of the researchers at the lab, he said, "Think what these and other instruments are already telling us about life on this planet! *This* is where the action is—right here on earth."

So it is. A deep-sea camera recently clicked pictures at a depth of about 16,000 feet in lightless high-pressure zones on the abyssal plains at the bottom of the Atlantic Ocean, and when the film was developed there stood a strange animal. It was a long-stemmed polyp, a relative of the jellyfish called *Umbellulidae,* and it resembles a wand with a snowflake on the end. The crystal-like appendages are feet that grab prey and stuff them into a mouth in the middle of the flake.

The beautiful creature was photographed by Walter Jahn, a specialist working for the Naval Oceanographic Office aboard the reaserch ship *Kane.* The only previous knowledge of this beast was scant. In the 1870s a British ship brought remains of this animal to the surface, and several years ago a Danish crew dredged up one that glowed blue before it faded and died. The strobe-light camera, however, revealed that the animal stands three feet tall and remains rooted to the earth on its stem.

The coasts of southwest Africa, where thundering waves crash into the rocks, is an environment that man could not probe until modern equipment made it possible in 1969. Here another weird earthling—the clingfish—was found. To withstand that pounding environment, the animal has evolved its belly fin into a powerful sucker that holds it to the boulders. The slender fish, icthyologists report, is related to another specialized fish, *Diademichthys lineatus,* an ingenious fellow that lives in the poisonous spines of an Indo-Pacific sea urchin.

Each of these relatives evolved totally different abilities in order to survive.

There is no guessing where some strange species may be found. A new earth migrant, the hydromedusa, was recently found in a modern trawl used to hunt the muddy bottom of waterways. A jellyfish cousin, this animal was thought to be a resident of the Black Sea and only the Black Sea. Yet it turned up in the equipment of a Virginia Institute of Marine Science ship while the crew was studying the bottom of the Chesapeake Bay. It had never before been seen in those waters, or for that matter anywhere in the Western Hemisphere. The research team suspects that the new citizen rode to Virginia on a ship, but how an animal that dies in salty water managed the ocean voyage is a secret that still belongs to the hydromedusa.

Even more unexpected animals have recently been detected growing in metal. Until just about yesterday it was believed that metals were an environment for *no* animal. They even killed bacteria. Yet, in the Chemical Laboratory at the University of Kent, England, a speck of a creature called *Escherichia coli* thrives and grows on platinum. Others have been found living out their rugged lives, eating and multiplying within the stifling environment of metals in jet fuel tanks.

Modern life hunters have not only discovered new animals, but unlocked the tricks of old familiar ones. For years men pondered how the hermit crab managed to pick sea anemones from the rocks and plant them on their shells for camouflage and protection. No man had been able to accomplish this. Merely touching one of these flower-like animals makes it hold tighter, and when forcibly removed it pulls apart rather than give up its grip on a rock. In the Zoology Lab at the University of Alberta, Edmonton, Canada, however, scientists are now picking up sea anemones as the crabs do by applying mechanical and electrical taps to them which causes the creatures to relax, release their grip, and detach. The stimulus is presented at the rate of one beat per second at the base of the anemones. Within three minutes they let go. Since these crabs steal anemones from each other, and it is even more difficult to remove them from shell than from rock, the Canadians studied the crabs and are now able to do this too.

*Hermit crab picking an anemone*

Using pipe cleaners, electricity, and the precise and mystical rhythm, one beat per second, they relax the anemones, lift them from one hermit's shell and put them down on another's.

Out of the sea and into the labs came another common creature, the barnacle, with incredible results. To fasten itself to ships and pilings the beast can make glue that is twice as tough as epoxy, binds together any materials, and resists all chemicals known to science. At 662° F. the barnacle glue softens only slightly; at −383° below zero it does not crack or peel. A mere 3/10,000 of an inch of barnacle material provides a sheer strength of over three tons (epoxy has about one and a half tons) and holds tighter than scientists have been able to measure. They believe that if a whole barnacle could be pulled from a steel buoy a layer of steel would come with it.

Prying into this wonder of nature, Dr. Roger Kelly of the University of Akron, Ohio, is bent on making the glue synthetically for many purposes but primarily for dental use. There is as yet no glue that can hold a filling permanently except perhaps that from the glands of the barnacle. These glands appear at the final larval stage of the barnacle's life when it is ready to give up its period of free wandering and settle down. At this point, it approaches an object, strikes it head first, the cement pours forth, and the glands then disappear. For the remainder of its life, it stands on its head kicking its feet in the water to direct food to a mouth in the midst of those feet. As it grows, it recreates the glands to cement down new shell. The Akron laboratory has isolated in the gland two fluids, one a milky white that is probably the shell builder, the other, a pale brown fluid as thick as motor oil which may be the cement machine. The next step is to analyze what the thick brown "motor oil" is and reproduce it synthetically for man's use, a science called bionics.

The study of animal life reaches into ever-expanding frontiers. Through an instrument called a hydrophone, or underwater ears, Roger Payne of the Rockefeller University, New York, heard for the first time the opera star of the ocean. In 1969 when he was making recordings of undersea noises off the coast of Bermuda, he was astonished to hear a long and beautiful aria floating in to him through the phones. The song came from between two thousand to four thousand feet, where a layer of water is so constituted that sounds spread out in two dimensions rather than three. In this "sound channel" voices travel far, and here in spring the humped-back whales sing to each other across great distances.

The squeals, squeaks, and groans of these whales had been heard before, but no man knew, until Payne listened through the hydrophones, that they sang. The songs are not brief like those of birds, which mostly are two to three seconds in duration, but are quite intricate, lasting from eight to thirty minutes. When one song is done, the whale begins again, repeating the same tune as he follows some coveted musical score of his race.

Insight into life need not always be gained through complicated instruments in remote areas. One of the most breathtaking inquiries is so common-place that I wonder why it has gone unnoticed for so long—the language of squirrels, messages sent through the woodland by the flick of a tail, the twist of an ear. For years I have watched gray squirrels cavorting through my yard and up my trees without knowing that those flashing tails are a semaphore, the sound of those pattering feet on dry leaves a Morse code. A translation of squirrel signals by Jan C. Taylor, of the Ministry of Agriculture in Surrey, England, was published in 1966. Newly informed, that spring I spent an entire afternoon in the woods by the lake trying to interpret an antagonistic conversation between several squirrels. The most conspicuous is the chase, and I had hardly settled myself among the mosses and ferns than down a tree trunk came two males running at full speed. They struck the ground with noisy thuds and clattered the leaves more than usual as they raced toward me. About ten feet away, the pursuer cut off the pursued and both stopped. Their language was clearly evident once I knew what to look for. The pursuer spoke to the other squirrel of his dominance and sex by narrowing his eyes and bringing his ears forward to expose a puff of white fur. The other said he was subdominant by opening his eyes wide and lowering his ears to his head. With that the boss squirrel lifted the hairs of his tail. The other answered by dropping the hairs of his. This encouraged the boss to announce his superior status, which he did by chattering his teeth, a signal that should have sent the other scurrying away. It did not, so the boss squirrel threatened him with what is comparable to poking a loaded gun in a man's face— he tore off strips from a green twig. That did it. Terrified, the pursued darted straight past him and off through the woods screaming in a high-pitched growl.

The boss, confident of his position, started up a tree just as a third squirrel spoke with a flick of the tail. Apparently he indicated his youth and insecurity, for the dominant squirrel lifted his ears, narrowed his eyes, and chased him.

The May bloodroots were star-white, the new leaves jewel green; I suddenly felt the urge to join the conversation and I clicked my tongue at the boss of the local squirrel world, who was sitting on his haunches listening to the others. I must have said something provocative for the squirrel came down to all fours and gingerly walked toward me sniffing and twirling his whiskers. I longed for a tail to flash, but having none, patted the leaves briskly. He stopped abruptly, lifted the hairs of his tail, and I knew he was telling me many things: sex, age, rank, perhaps even that he had a family nearby. I tapped the leaves again. This time I evidently said something horrible, for he screamed a piercing warning cry. He paddled his feet, then turned and sped up a maple. His message reached the ears of the other two squirrels; they stopped their chase and put a tree between themselves and me. They repeated his cry and were answered by leafy footsteps deeper in the woods, perhaps their mates. Then the forest became silent.

What had I said? I was thrilled as I envisioned the day when a man could tell a squirrel exactly where he had left some nuts for him, or the squirrel would tell the man there is a snake in the trail. Science fiction? Not at all, just one of the many new relationships that we may enjoy as science opens new doors on this earth.

# CHAPTER 2

# SCULPTORS OF INCREDIBLE
# FORM AND FEATURE

THE old Paris Museum of Natural History was an elaborate building that faced a tree-lined mall where house sparrows chirped and bathed in the dust and pigeons drank from the waters of a fountain. People sat on benches, children played French singing games, but few went into the dark museum.

Early one Monday morning long ago, while my fellow students were off on the Left Bank collecting objects of art, I climbed the steps to the institution and went in to see what it held. I had been told by a French mammalogist that it could not compare with the Museum of Natural History in New York, but this did not deter me. A museum of nature was to me like an old attic to a book collector.

As my heels clanked and echoed through an enormous corridor, I thought for a moment that the museum might be all walls and gloom. Then I rounded a corner and entered a hall almost as large as the rotunda of Grand Central Station in New York. The expanse of creatures seemed boundless—dust-laden, moth-eaten, but glorious. I had never seen so many in one room, and I realized for the first time how crowded with varied life the earth really is. Deer, squirrels, tigers, bats, whales, and rodents were assembled before me like an enormous silent circus.

Their shapes and sizes were more imaginative than I had ever comprehended by looking at books or visiting zoos. Long necks loomed over short ones, fat legs stood beside slender ones, ears dropped in tiny flaps or lifted like trumpets, and flat torsos huddled near rotund bellies. All morning I wandered in and out of the hundreds of beasts, examining thousands more in cases around the balcony. This old place offered a unique experience to me, as I became self-conscious of my own 206 bones and 650 muscles. Man has much in common with other creatures that spring from the simple formula of life. Through other doors, down other corridors, were cases upon cases of birds, reptiles, and fishes. Their diversity of shape and design was staggering.

When I came to the invertebrates—insects, shells, corals, sponges, crustaceans—the configurations were so different that I took three turns around these halls and still could not grasp the singularity of life.

Diversity is an odd way to begin a collection, but as I circled the museum I made categorical notes of some creatures I should track down. Exaggerated appendages like the noses of anteaters proclaimed an odd way of life—but how did they get that way? What forces, what materials were used to shape these beasts?

Walking back to my hotel, I became aware that although the Paris Museum of Natural History might be out-dated, it presents every visitor a staggering question in a way that no other museum does. In room after room the ears, coils, fans, beaks, fins drive home the question of what it is that shapes the formula of life into 250 million astonishing forms.

J. Z. Young, professor of anatomy at the University College, London, pointed out that the arrangement of the skeleton and muscles of mammals differs according to the habits and the environment in which each species of animal lives. He noted that even during the brief lifetime of one individual animal, the force of gravity imposes a varying stress on the tissues of the body, causing it to conform to the particular conditions that it meets. Here then, are the sculptors—the environment and the substances of life. Our own muscles and bones have provided the means by which the body can be supported in various positions against the force of gravity. As we seek food and shelter, we are sculptured by our needs and emerge from the environmental studio erect, head balanced over our bodies, arms free to pick up loads, knees straight, feet flat and primitive for walking. As we are shaped, so is all life honed by environments and the animal tissue reacting to them.

The wizardry of bone and muscle tissues is that it combines maximum strength with minimum weight to counteract gravity. An animal that runs like the deer does not put the stress on the same tissues that we who walk do. A running animal will get up on its toes, the best position for speed, and the bone tissues of the legs and feet will answer the change of stress. They will straighten the heel and develop a hoof as the body puts pressure on the toe and ultimately on the toenail, as in the leaping, running deer. No machine can perform as it does. As the tissue responds to the environment and to the animal, a beast becomes more specialized through natural selection to eventually vary from others in his class.

What is tissue that it can be shaped into so many marvelous forms? It is a region of similar cells that perform the same function and are bound together by intercellular material called collagen. After my tour of the Paris Museum I became far more interested in collagen, that mechanical support for protoplasm that holds the beast in shape. One of the principal skeletal substances, it is the essence of cell membranes, bones, feathers, hair, and claws.

With this in mind, I began to build files about those animals that had done the most spectacular sculpturing with collagen, and the birds came first.

Buried in the skin of a bird is a highly specialized scale

*Reeves pheasant: longest tail, fastest plunge*

that has gone through a process of evolution, finally emerging and breaking into the delicate parts of the feather. Its main stem or shaft is hollow for buoyancy, and the barbs that grow out from it, the web or vane, can make the finest adjustments to air and wind. In addition, the feather is still the best insulation known. When groomed correctly, feathers keep a bird warm in subzero weather, and cool at 110° F. As we know, they take many shapes. There is down contour feathers that overlap the body like weather-proof shingles; filoplumes, which look like hair, but grow (among other places) at the base of the contour of tail feathers and wing feathers; and bristles that grow around the nostrils of the bird. The stress of gravity, the varied environments and the needs of the bird, have brought into existence some unique feathers. The enormous, exquisite display of the peacock seems all the more fantastic to the scientist who knows how this came about. Through the pressures and uses exerted upon them, the upper tail coverts enlarged into great iridescent feathers until they far exceeded the real tail feathers that lie under them.

The tails of other birds have been modified into tools. The frigatebird and barn swallow have developed forked tails to give greater leverage for making quick changes in flight direction. Woodpeckers have rigid points at the tip of the two central tail feathers that act as braces against trees. The longest feathers on earth are the two very practical central pairs in the tail of the Reeve's pheasant, a species that lives in the wooded mountain valleys of central western China. Over eight feet long, they propel the bird twice as fast as the common pheasant, and they look like meteor tails in the sky, for they gleam bright orange-red in color. In an environment of cliffs, forests, and predators, they also serve to brake the pheasant in mid-air, to cause it to plummet straight down to the cover of the trees. To do this, the birds throw their tails up vertically, turn the expanded surface sharply against the oncoming air, and plunge as if felled by a shot.

Another unusual feather has been evolved by the herons, bitterns, hawks and woodswallows: powder down. Somewhat oily, the tip breaks up into a powder that can be used by the young birds to lubricate the rest of their plumage. For the first few months of life, when the oil glands of fledglings are too undeveloped to exude oil, the powder feathers act as a substitute.

Just as there is a bird with the longest feather there is one that appears to have the most feathers, because they are so fluffy. This is the great grey owl, the largest one in North America, who dwells in the boreal forests of New Hampshire, along the northern border of California, and in Idaho and Wyoming. A dusky, elongate ball, he has a black chin, enormous round head, and a facial disc marked with dark lines. He stands almost three feet high and a foot or more wide, which is a gross deception. One summer while visiting my brothers in Wyoming I came around the pumphouse to find their pet great grey bathing in the irrigation ditch. He had soaked himself flat to the skin and, as I watched, he pulled his sodden body to shore with his beak. There he rotated his head and looked up at me from a chicken-sized body. Usually, when I stuck my fingers into his feathers to scratch his skull, my hand sank into the mid-palm, so well-feathered is this owl.

Insects have their own version of collagen—chitin, a material similar to collagen. It is a nitrogen containing polysaccharide with long fibrous molecules, of great mechanical strength, and resistant to chemicals. Chitin is the outside covering of insects, which serves as an external skeleton in place of an internal one like our own. From this material, they have fashioned a variety of remarkable tools, pinchers, music boxes, amplifiers, drills, hooks, levers, wings. The air-breathing water scorpion lives under water by breathing through two snorkels of chitin extending from its breathing organs. One of the great sculptors of chitin is probably the most common pest alive, the rain barrel mosquito, whose most astonishing features were unknown until recently.

Through chitin-covered antennae the females, who need a drop of blood to develop eggs (males do not bite), detect from considerable distance carbon dioxide emitted by the breathing of man or beast.

It is the chitin beak or "needle" of this insect, however, that is the wonder. It pierces skin that must be near or over ninety degrees (human skin averages from eighty-seven to ninety-five degrees). Inside the flesh the hard chitin bends and twists as it literally "looks" for a capillary. When a blood vessel is located, the beak stiffens, pierces, bends again, and moves along the tube as much as a quarter of its length. Pumps in the female's abdomen start to work, and blood is withdrawn in amounts that are almost twice the insect's weight. When replete the pumps are turned off, the female pushes down on her chitin-covered feet and withdraws her needle.

So flourishing is the mosquito that species of it dwell the world around, from the Arctic to the Antarctic, wherever its victims are to be found.

Mollusks—that great phylum of seashell creatures (including clams and oysters)—have "sculptured" with calcium so abundantly that there is often more shell than animal. The stony shell, which is composed of purer calcium carbonate than any rock in the hills, is built from within. The dissolved calcium in sea water is sucked through a syphon into the mollusk's stomach and dispersed to the mantel, a soft layer of cells lining the shell. How the mollusk controls these mantels is a mystery to us. Each species has a memory code of its own that puts down the calcium in colors, ripples, and whorls. All together they create more than 75,000 different shapes, each determined according to depth of sea water, temperature, pressure, wave action—all the physical elements that make up the thousands of sea environments.

Creating shell is but one of the achievements of the

mollusk. Sometime in the distant past, the squid and the octopus, also members of this phylum, were differently influenced by the sea. The shell-building genes died out and the genes of the soft tissues shaped creatures that were unrecognizable as mollusks except by embryologists, who found vestiges of their ancient shell-building cells in the embryos of these fleshy animals.

In giving up a protective shell, the squid and octopus developed protective eyes from the primitive light-sensitive cells that lie on the mantels of other mollusks. Their eyes are more nearly like our own than any other eyes on earth. These animals not only see color, but detail, focusing on an object by moving their eyes in and out like a telescope.

Several years ago at the Lerner Marine Laboratory in Bimini in the Bahamas, a pair of these eyes met mine. I was spending a few days in the library, and upon learning one morning that a female octopus lived on the premises, I hastily dropped my work and went to see her.

Behind the main building stood a line of salt-water tanks. A young man, arms folded belligerently over his chest, stared into one of them. I peered into the tank to see a small species of octopus humped in a corner. To my surprise she was without water, and I expressed my concern.

"She pulled out the plug," the young man snapped. "She always does that. No matter how tightly I put it in, she pries it right out with her discs." He reached toward the plug tentatively; the eyes slid in as they kept his hand in focus. Then a tentacle slashed out and he withdrew. "I never knew a nastier beast. I hate her!" he said and went for the forceps.

Chuckling at his defeat I glanced down at the irritable wonder. Slowly her eyes turned upon me and I grew cold as this offshoot of the lowly clam stared at me with the eyes of mankind. I hurried back to the library. Whenever I think of that incident, I am always struck with the same uneasy feeling.

In the sea, the problem of gravity is not as great as it is on land, and some animals can exist without either outer or inner skeletons. The buoyant water becomes their support and their tissues are specialized for floating. The genius of this environment is the jellyfish, which has captured water inside itself, making a body just a little less dense than its home.

Ninety-five percent of the jellyfish is water, a percentage that prevents it from either bobbing on the top or sinking to the bottom, but holds it just under the surface of the sea. Whenever I see jellyfish, I feel compelled to go through the same experiment. I drag one up on the beach above the tide-mark, mark it with a stick, and return a day or so later. I always find that there remains a faint trace of salts where I left the bulky creature. Evaporated, the animal is barely a shadow in an eerie hollow in the sand where its weight once made an imprint.

The jellyfish, however, is beautifully adapted to the sea. Scattered through it are ameboid cells and tough fibers that hold the water so firmly that the animal can drift in storms, crash against rocks, and survive in all seas. It dwells from the tumultuous Arctic waters to seemingly jelly-melting warmth of tropical oceans.

Most of these creatures are small, from a quarter of an inch to five inches (2 to 40 cm). This being so, one would suspect that the more violent the seas, the smaller the jellyfish, but this does not follow. *Cynea artica,* the largest, dwells near the rocky shores of the Arctic Ocean in waters rough and destructive. The bell of this animal is often seven feet across, the tentacles thirty feet long. Like the umbrella jellyfish of the Atlantic and Pacific coasts, the *Cyanea* has evolved mechanisms to protect it from danger. Muscle-like tissues contract its umbrella, push out the sea water, and drive it gently forward. Then the bell fills and the great jellyfish contracts to move again. One can only wonder how tissue, brainless and unthinking, could be so controlled.

Another material out of which unusual shapes are formed

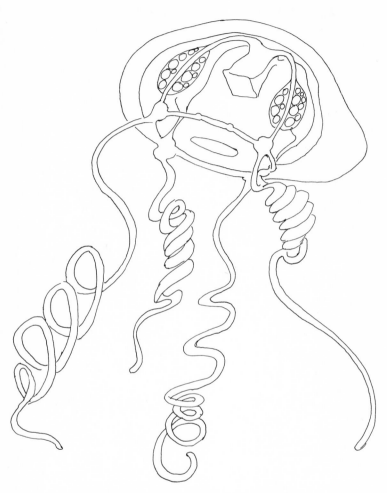

*Medusa of Eucopium—mostly water*

is the single animal, which acts as though it were a cell. By adding one individual to another and another, a colony is built. That is how corals and sponges are formed. Fan, tree, basket, cylinder—whatever shapes these colonies assume—each is composed of thousands of individual animals to which we give a single name: the brain coral, the bathtub sponge, the dead man's finger.

Not only do these groups look like one animal, but they have arranged themselves so ingeniously that parts of the colony perform bodily functions for the whole. An individual sponge animal does not have a respiratory or excretory mechanism, but together they do. They arrange themselves in such a way that they leave one or more holes in the colony. Through these flows a constant stream of water that brings oxygen and food to the individuals and carries off their carbon dioxide and nitrogenous wastes. When the animals die, a collagen-like material called sponin remains. Sponin is a hard material that is shaped like rods, spikes, and stars, but together forms fans, cups, and flowers—beautiful brittle shapes for seaside collectors.

Although most sponges and corals are immobile, like the octopus of the mollusk family, there is one that listens to a different drummer. The sulphur sponge and its family can drill. It comes to rest on oysters and clams and grows until it looks like a yellow wart. At this stage it drills by rubbing the sponin, an instrument as effective as a steel bit, into the shell. After killing the mollusk, it evacuates it, then grows out from the shell, sometimes attaining a massive form three feet wide. To fishermen of the Delaware Bay and the bays near Sea Island, New Jersey, these flowers of "yellow coral" (they are yellow but not coral) mean good fishing. Tenanted by sea organisms that live in their holes, the sulphur sponges attract fish, which attract bigger fish, which attract fishermen.

The individuals of a sponge colony transcend our wildest medical dreams of restoring maimed bodies. Not long ago at the Woods Hole Marine Biological Laboratory, Massachusetts, a friend startled me by demonstrating this uncanny ability of the sponge. She took one from a tank, asked me to study it carefully and draw what I saw. It was a species called the red sponge, having four clusters of slender fingers and three irregular holes. When I finished my sketch, she forced the animal through a piece of silk, breaking it into thousands of parts. They floated like a mist in a finger bowl. "Come back in a day," she said, for she is a scientist who does not spoil the excitement of personal discovery for anyone. As I departed I imagined that I would see hundreds of red sponges starting new colonies.

What I saw still taxes my credulity. I found one sponge, the very same one that I had seen her shove through the silk. Comparing it with my drawing, I recognized the same animal. Looking out over the bay, I tried to imagine the environmental forces and the magic in tissues that were reacting to them that could bring Humpty Dumpty together again. The MBL scientists also wonder. Several students are presently studying the cells to find out what reassembles them.

Perhaps even with the sponge to aid our imagination, the most difficult to understand is the group organism of the honey bee. About seven years ago, it was discovered that the hive is not the residence of a social colony in the usual sense, but a single animal of many glittering parts. An infant in the swarming stage, it progresses from adolescence to maturity, gives birth to new hives, and finally subsides in the quietude of winter. It even grows old and dies.

Bee experts came to this conclusion when they noted that a hive of bees can actually suffer wounds, moan in agony and then, in its drive to live, repair itself like any other feverish animal.

Each bee, like the parts of a body, has a function to perform. The drone is the sperm of life, the queen, the reproductive organ. The workers (females that do not reproduce) develop through many stages of work. The youngest attend the queen and feed her; they grow up to clean the hive. Later they shake thin sheaths from the abdomen and chew them into wax. Some become guards at this stage and stand at the door to keep off robber bees and animals. After twenty-three days they are old enough to leave the hive and forage for nectar.

While experimenting, a European scientist removed the wax makers from a hive and found that the older foragers ceased to hunt food. They came back to the hive, were rejuvenated, and made wax again. When a Russian entomologist removed a queen from a hive the impossible happened. Within several days, a few workers began to lay eggs, laboriously, slowly, one or two a day, in contrast to the three thousand of the queen.

This piqued the interest of C. R. Ribbands of England. He saw that just as a wound in our flesh is healed, a wound in the bee hive is healed, a miracle that meant to him that the many individuals were one living system. Ribbands looked for some common ingredient like blood that linked the bees together. After long observation he came to the conclusion that this blood is honey. It flows to all parts of the hive, from nurse to hive cleaner, to wax maker, to forager, then back from the foragers to the hive cleaner, wax maker, nurse, and queen. The honey moved like the fluid in our bodies that circulates from the heart through all our organs and back again. When the queen was taken away, the enzyme she gave the honey was missing. The absence of this ingredient was sensed by the workers, and they fought their disease of queenlessness by transforming themselves into egg layers. Such is the genius of nature.

CHAPTER 3

# *INGENIOUS WAYS TO TRAVEL*

I HAD never thought much about ways animals get around, beyond swimming, walking, and flying, until I saw a hydra, a fresh-water jellyfish-like creature, in a lab at the University of Michigan. A graduate student had brought in several from a field trip and had placed them in a shallow glass aquarium. They were quite small and transparent, an animal difficult to find in the streams and pools in which they live, so I hung over them curiously as they moved their tentacles and stretched in search of food. Each stood on a trunk and looked more like a palm tree than a beast except that in the center of the tentacles was a mouth. As I looked through a magnifying glass, one of them leaned over, placed its tentacles on the bottom of the aquarium, lifted its trunk straight up, and stood on its head. The trunk then hesitated, bent to the ground and the tentacles were up again. It put its "hands" down again. With that I called excitedly to the graduate student, "It's turning cart wheels!"

"In cart wheels," he called back, "the hydra travels." I was launched on a search for odd travelers.

The hydra, which can be found on every continent, is a simple beast with but two layers of building cells, the outer or ectoderm, the inner or endoderm. Within the endoderm are long contractible muscles. When these are tightened

27

*The walking hydra*

equally on all sides, the hydra shortens. When they contract more on one side than the other, the body bends in the direction of the greatest contraction, and if motivated to move will put its "hands" down and turn cart wheels. After a few acrobatics, the hydra reaches a new destination. It travels when the water temperature is too high or the oxygen supply depleted; it moves toward light where there is generally more food.

Another species of hydra with longer tentacles "chins" itself to new places. It reaches out with its tentacles, takes hold of an object, lets go of its base, and contracting its body pulls itself up to the object. Still another uses a gas balloon. It departs for better conditions by manufacturing a gas bubble from glands on its basal disc. When the bubble is ready, it lets go and bobs to the surface. Here it floats about upside down, disengaging the bubble when ready to sink.

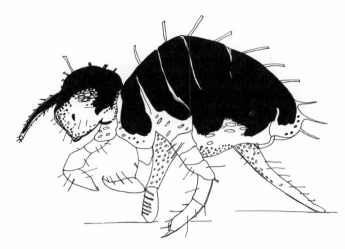

*Springtail with its pogo stick*

Biologists who pry into behavior of travel are generally men who enjoy the ingenuity of animals, and when I mentioned the hydra to an entomologist he told me to study the springtail. "It travels on a kind of sophisticated pogo stick." The next spring I acquired a springtail and looked through a book on entomology to find out about it. Tiny creatures less than one-sixteenth of an inch long, they can be either naked, hairy, or scaly, but all jump hundreds of times their own height, not with legs like a flea, but on a spring-like mechanism that lies on the underside of the abdomen. This device, called a furculum, is a pair of partially fused appendages that fork at the end and are held in the belly by a trigger-like catch. When it is motivated to travel, the springtail unlocks the catch, the furculum flies out with force, strikes the ground or water, and sends the springtail vaulting two, even three, feet in the air. They are little marvels. Feeding on disintegrated organic matter, they can be seen by the hundreds on a summer day on the surface of ponds or the quiet pools of a stream leaping on their "pogo sticks." Some appear on the snow in late February and early March, for they are one of the first insects abroad in spring. They are also one of the earth's homeliest creatures; their backs are humped, their faces elongated, droll as an image in a fun-house mirror.

To travel by dislocating the back is the invention of the click or elater beetles. Known in the larval stage as "wire worms," they are both serious pests and useful predators, for although they eat roots of crops, they also devour the destructive white grubs and other insect larvae in the ground.

When mature they are beautiful elongate beetles that hurry recklessly over grasses and leaves. So headlong do they run that they frequently tumble over and for some reason or other land on their backs. To travel on, they dislocate a ball from a socket in the back that lies between the first thoracic segment and the second, where the wings are attached. Unhinged, they bridge into an arch, then jam the process together with such force that they vault into the air with a click. Several feet above the ground they right themselves and come back to earth on their feet. So much is this flip a part of their lives that I have seen some fly into the air three or four times in the course of a short scurry through the border of my garden.

The propelling power of falling water has not gone unnoticed by the travelers. Along the continental shelves of the world, sanddollars, starfish, and sea urchins ply their way by means of hydraulic pressure known as the "water vascular system." More like a Rube Goldberg invention than a life system, the walking mechanism of these Echinoderms is one of the marvels of the animal kingdom.

Water enters the starfish, for example, through tiny openings in the middle of the topside, the sieve plate. It falls down a well where its speed is increased by the swirling action of cilia or hairs that grow below the sieve. Forced down a tube of calcareous rings, the stone canal, the water rips along and enters the ring canal, a circular pipe from which arise five

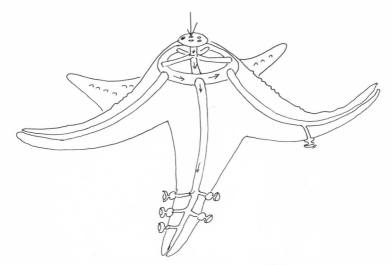

*Hydraulic system of the starfish*

radial canals, one for each arm. (All Echinoderms have five parts, arranged radially, which are more easily seen in the starfish than the sanddollars and sea urchins.)

The radial canals run to the many pairs of hollow tube feet which have suckers on the outside. Inside the tube foot is a valve and a balloon-like sac. The water enters the foot and after the valve closes is forced into the sac, expanding. Then a squeeze from muscles in the sac shoots the water out the tube foot. The shot pushes the tube foot forward and slaps the sucker against the rocks or sand.

The fantastic step is not yet complete. Well-anchored by the sucker, the tube foot next contracts and forces the water back into the balloon sac, and it is this contraction that pulls the animal forward.

One such movement does not get the starfish very far, but with hundreds of feet, all squeezing and contracting, the animal moves slowly over the ocean floor.

The power of this mechanism is so tremendous that a starfish can open a clam, a job that requires a man to use a strong knife. Using its hydraulic feet in many relays, the starfish keeps suction pressure on the shell. After about ten to thirty minutes, the two large muscles that hold the clam so tightly together, relax from fatigue, and the shells part.

Sea urchins, those beautiful pincushions of the sea floors of the world, occasionally creep but more often use the hydraulic pressure system to swing their spines and sting food. One species, however, when under stress, can lift loads with this system. Off the coast of South America a night-loving sea urchin hides in deep water to avoid the light. A student observing them by night with a flashlight so upset them that they lowered their spines and slowly lifted pebbles to cut off the light. One, he reports, held five above its body until he turned his flashlight off and sat back to wonder how a sea urchin could know that a pebble can cast a shadow.

Water animals travel through that heavy medium usually on smooth, compact bodies that glide, like the fish and whales. Backswimmers, however, are insects that have discovered the virtue of oars and a keel. Their third set of legs is elongated

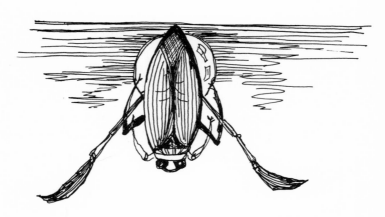

*Backswimmer, with oars and bubble*

and rounded at the ends; their backs are shaped into a ship's bottom. With these devices they travel, as their name denotes, on their backs, darting swiftly through the water by pulling on their oars and staying upright (upside down is right side up to them) on their keels.

When not rowing, the backswimmers hang head down from the surface of the water, their breathing organs thrust into the air, their long oars pointed downward. At the least disturbance they will place their other two pairs of legs in such a way that a bubble of water forms around their breathing organs. Taking this diving bell with them, they row to the bottom with swift jerky movements, grab a plant with strong front feet that are designed to capture small fishes and tadpoles, and hang one. When ready to surface they let go and pop up on the bubble. A member of the water bug family (water creatures with sucking beaks), the backswimmers live in protected pools where plants are dense and the litter of dead vegetation and its attendant food is abundant.

The larva of the moth *Elophila fulicalis* moves around the bottom of ponds and streams by yet another method. A row of plumes grows from each side of this insect and these it flaps and twirls like the wings on a mechanical bird.

Another strange traveling device is the water jet of the nymphs of the damsel and dragonflies. These expel water from the anus, an action that catapults them forward. In their anal chambers are a lacework of air or breathing tubes that needs a constant supply of fresh, aeriated water. The tubes are controlled by muscles along the chamber wall. Given these, it is not surprising that when the animals are frightened they clamp down on the muscles, create a jet of water, and zoom away from trouble.

While collecting in a Connecticut stream not long ago, I saw that I had a dragonfly nymph in my bucket and reached toward it. It did not jet away, but turned on its back and played dead by bending its legs double and folding its huge trap-door mouth parts against its head. When I touched it, however, it came to life, clamped down on its anal muscles, and shot across the bottom of the bucket. Later, unthreatened and feeling secure, it prowled on its six feet, using the anal jet to help it over obstacles.

Glorious is the vehicle of the spiderlings. These little creatures go ballooning on the spring and autumn air. When the warmth of the sun brings them out of an egg sac by the hundreds, the spiderlings do not linger near each other for fear of being eaten, but disperse, running swiftly up stems and over leaves to the very tips of plants.

At the end of the climb they face in the direction of the wind and spin silver threads from their spinnerettes (up to eight in number depending on the species). Drawn out on the breeze, the thread is eventually long enough to lift the tiny spiderling from its mooring and carry it through the air.

Each of the many ballooning species travels in a different way. In most cases, once launched they turn around and climb their threads, reefing in here, letting out there as they maneuver their two to three yards of silver line like a sailor on the sea. With pulls and tugs they sail around twigs and corners of houses. Some are not quick enough and crash land on trees. When this happens they scurry to the tip of a leaf, throw out threads, and take off again. They go far and high. Spiderlings have been found on ships two hundred miles from land or caught in powerful air currents ten thousand feet above the earth.

Ballooning is not confined to the spiderlings. Some species will sail in their maturity. That ground lover, the stocky jumping spider, will balloon in the presence of strong wind or when a human blows at it. It will turn, throw up its rear end at an amusing angle, spin, and take off.

The air is full of spider travelers riding their magic carpets to new destinations, according to an aerial survey taken in

1918. Sixty-nine species were found aloft. When they touch down, spiders usually abandon their silver balloons, and the gossamer blows on with the wind, coming down upon the earth in some distant place. Sometimes it collects in great sheets, as it does in the Yosemite Valley of California, where stone arches make natural traps for the wind. Here the webbing descends on trees, limbs, and foliage in such abundance that the landscape looks like sheet-covered furniture in a deserted house.

Snakes are remarkable in that they travel with no more than hinged plates, which they use in several ways. The most common action is called the "lateral undulatory movement." In this process the entire body twists on the ground, an action that pushes up piles of dirt. From these piles the snake pivots and thereby goes forward. If in vegetation, the plants and leaf litter serve as pivots.

The "caterpillar movement," an up and down motion employed by large rattlesnakes, is achieved by pressing down on scutes or belly plates. The front of each is hidden under the hind edge of the one in front; the side edges are loosely attached to the ends of the ribs. The plates are then moved a few at a time, for if they were all moved at once the rattler would go backward, not forward. Beginning under the neck the wave moves down the belly, one undulation following another as the hind edges of the plates catch on every projection and send the snake forward.

In the desert where the sand gives way and the scutes slip, the sidewinder rattlesnake has found a startling way to travel. The sand is used simply to support the weight of the snake's body as it lunges forward in a spiral. By making himself into a coil of two or three loops, the sidewinder can press down on the scutes on the bottom of each coil and shoot along the ground like a wire coil that does not roll, but skids forward on the bottom of the loops.

Another snake "swims" in sand—the banded burrowing snake of lower California. This reptile sinks just beneath the surface of the desert sands and, employing the lateral undulatory movement, moves as if in water.

A toy has always delighted me because it applies a physical principle that demonstrates man's reasoning powers. It is a little doll that balances on the edges of a cup with a long curved stick and two heavy balls that throw the center of gravity far enough below it to keep the doll balanced despite pushes and jolts.

The doll is not so special, however. The boa has been using the same principle for eons, long before man walked the earth. To prevent itself from falling the tree-traveling boa drapes parts of its body below a limb to keep its center of gravity low. These snakes can also cross wide spaces without drooping by applying other principles of balance. Taking a firm hold on a limb by coiling, they let themselves out more than two-thirds of their length on a horizontal plane, the

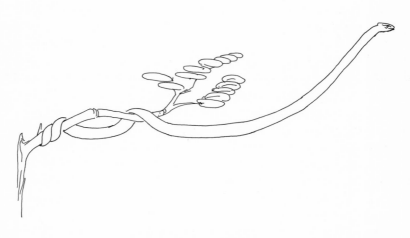

*How the boa travels*

weight plus the strength behind always being more than that being extended. Upon reaching another limb they coil around it and slide until the tail is lighter and can be pulled across without falling.

Our own black snakes, blue racers, and coach whips glide through bushes and briar patches by extending, balancing, and shifting, but they cannot compare to the boas who seem that they must fall as they stretch out to travel.

Although the snake has a reputation of being a swift beast, actually it is not. The fastest in this country is the western whip snake, a creature that travels only three miles an hour when frightened and about a quarter of a mile per hour when prowling.

Snakes have still another way of traveling, as seen by the entire family of jumping vipers of the American tropics. They are terrifying creatures that horrify men as they spring out of the vegetation and, wingless, armless, footless, take to the air. The carpet viper of Africa north of the equator, also a jumper, coils into a spring, releases himself, and leaps from one limb to another like a Jack-in-the-box.

Travel reaches its apogee in the birds. Freed from the earth, unencumbered by the land environment, birds are the earth's unsurpassed travelers. In order to fly with the winds they have adapted living parts that are more wondrous than our finest planes. Every twist of a bird's feather takes energy from the air and uses it to advantages no man-made craft can duplicate. Over the ages the weight and pressure of the air surrounding the living organism and the living needs and abilities to adapt have shaped birds (including flightless ones) into 8600 designs or species. With an innate understanding of air, the tissue of each feather responding, birds have discovered the most magnificent ways to lift and go forward, the essence of flight.

Streamlined in form, they move along the currents of the air always maneuvering to reduce the pressure on the surface of their wings and increase it underneath, for if ever the pressure became equal on both surfaces the bird would fall. It does not fall, however, for each group of feathers functions properly. The primary feathers that grow out of what is comparable to our forefingers are the propellers of the birds. These are swung in a semi-circle and back, an action that carries the bird forward as a propeller carries an airplane forward.

The secondary feathers that grow between the elbow and the wrist make up much of the lifting surface, for they move and drop like airplane wing flaps to increase the pressure on the underside of the wing. Between elbow and shoulder grow the tertiary feathers which refine the lifting. Scapulars cover the distance between the wing and body and complete the surface streamlining. Each feather is slightly different from the next, and each reacts to situations on its own—to make the bird the perfect creature of flight.

To many ornithologists and aeronautical engineers, no bird can match the wandering albatross of the windy South Atlantic. On wings of white, tipped with black, this living craft can glide for six days without beating a wing or coming down to rest. So adapted is this magnificent creature to the winds above the vast Atlantic that the young albatrosses leave the islands where they are born, South Georgia, Prince Edward, and Antipodes of the sub-Antarctic region, and do not touch land for two years.

The largest of any flying creatures alive from wing tip to wing tip, the albatross has a wing spread of from ten to twelve feet and is capable of circling the globe in normal cruising. In twelve days an albatross, with a dated message on a cord around its neck indicating where and when it had been set free, traveled 3150 miles!

These birds even sleep at night on the wing, taking advantage of the updraft from the waves as they rest over their watery home at speeds from nineteen to thirty-five miles per hour, a feat that is to them as natural as our breathing in sleep. Outwitted by the wind, the wandering albatross has more wing feathers than any other bird—eighty-eight as compared to fifty-six in an average bird.

Admiral William Jameson of the British Navy, who sailed into the windy home of the wandering albatross on H.M.S. *Ark Royal* in the early 1940s and observed them for months as they followed his ship south of the Cape of Good Hope, found that in calms they cannot fly but come down to sit on the ocean. In the wind, however, they put his ship to shame. On a day when the air currents were moving at forty knots and the waves were one hundred yards from crest to crest, the troughs fifteen feet deep, several wandering albatrosses overtook the *Ark Royal* speeding along at twenty-one miles per hour. Passing close by, one dashed ahead, banked in a trough, and emerged several minutes later facing into the strong wind. Gale notwithstanding, it settled back, crossed the wake of the ship, came around to the bow, and hung beside the Admiral peering at him curiously. "Not once did I see any of the birds flap their wings that day," he wrote, then marveled, "How does a bird regain the height it loses as it swoops down to water level, and why is it not swept bodily away to leeward in the wind?" Jameson added that while the ship traveled one mile, the birds traveled twelve.

Professor P. Idrac of the Ecole Polytechnique, Paris, recently studied the physics of the albatross to find principles applicable to aircraft. He concluded that they stay aloft without movement because they are "aerodynamically 'clean' and can fly at high speeds." Despite his mathematical equation, no man has built an albatross.

When they come down in a calm or to feed on the waves, the great birds are so adapted to the wind that they cannot get back on their wings unless the waves are moving steadily forward at twenty to thirty miles per hour. Such wave speed creates an updraft near the surface that gives them enough

*Hummingbird: upside down, backwards, dead center*

lift to get airborne with only a few wing beats. When waves are moving less than that, the birds flap heavily, and violently work their legs for at least a hundred yards before they can attain flying speed. One naturalist, Frank T. Bullen, visiting albatross country in 1904, reported that the "beating of their feet on the water is a sound that is audible a long way off."

Possibly because it takes time to develop the feathers and muscles necessary for this extraordinary flight, the young remain in the nest longer than any other bird—from nine to twelve months. Born in the summer, they spend the winter in ice-bound nests. The following summer they flap and exercise, run with wings extended, practice, jump, and finally get aloft by early autumn.

Just as the albatross is the earth's most perfect glider, the hummingbird is its most incredible stunt flyer. By maneuvering wing and feathers it can perform feats no man-made machine can begin to approach, for the hummingbird travels backward, forward, sidewise, and hovers in one place for more than an hour without showing the slightest sign of breathlessness or fatigue.

The smallest of these birds, the bee hummingbird of South America, a wisp of a thing no bigger than a large moth, can do all these aerial tricks plus a few more. Hanging stationary in the air, it will suddenly turn on its back and stand head up or head down according to its whims.

Our own ruby-throated hummingbird is no slouch. Aerial miracles were performed daily by a female that nested on the limb of my apple tree several years ago. Around seven o'clock one morning I saw her use herself as a drill as, wings buzzing, she drove her beak into the closed calyx of a trumpet-vine flower. After sipping the nectar she shot away backward. Her mate performed another unbelievable maneuver; he hovered before my glass window for several minutes to look at his reflection, then closed his wings, dropped straight down like a stone, opened them into a parachute near the ground and zoomed to the grape arbor. There, without slowing down, he went straight up in the air, forward, and over the vines to the woods.

On another occasion I happened to see the female go to and leave her nest in several maneuvers I still can hardly believe. The apple leaves hung low over her tiny nest, so she planed in horizontally forward. Under the leaf she hung in the air, wings buzzing. Then slowly, gently, she lowered herself onto her eggs without touching her feet down. Not until all her weight was eased upon her quarter-inch eggs did she stop winging and sit. About half an hour later, she started her wings again, slowly lifted herself until she cleared the nest rim, then shot out—backward.

On another occasion I approached the male from the front as he hung before a small bluebell. Seeing me, he rolled to his back by throwing his neck about his head and shot off upside down and backward. Above the garden he righted himself and flew off.

Slow motion movies have revealed that these birds perform these incredible maneuvers almost entirely with the wings. Their tail feathers scarcely move.

It is, however, the hummingbird's ability to hover that takes my breath. A Munich ornithologist picked up a caged South American hummingbird at the airport one day and, placing it beside him in the car, drove for an hour and a half to reach his home. During the entire trip the bird hung, wings whirling, in the absolute center of the cage even when he rounded corners or hit a bump. As it hung there, it turned its head from time to time to look at the man, never losing its dead center position, and it never sat down to rest.

The mechanical workings of the wings partially explain this exceptional flight, for the hummingbird's wings beat forward and backward, not up and down like those of other birds. Furthermore, each beat describes a figure eight to give these birds uninterrupted, vibration-free movement. To this is added an ability to keep the wings horizontal to the ground at all times, no matter which way the body is turned—upside down, right side up, or sidewise.

What environmental factors dictated the incomparable design of these birds? Perhaps the thousands of different flowers that the hummingbird must visit to take in more than half its body weight in nectar and insects each day is an answer. Flowers are hard to adjust to; some hang like bells, others open like platters, have whorls, or bloom at all angles to the earth. Could they be the sculptors of the hummingbird? I would like to think so.

Just as there are wings that are matchless, so are there feet—
the most provocative mammalian feet belonging to the bighorn sheep of our dry western mountains. These mammals
can dash headlong up cliffs, bound up boulders, jump wide
chasms, and do all at breakneck speeds. On their magic feet,
they can stop almost instantly and land their 350 pounds on
hard rock without shattering their bones and skulls.

How do they do it? They are artiodactyls, two-toed mammals that stand on their toenails—toenails that in their case
have been fused into a pair of pliers. The balls of their ankle
joints are rolling surfaces above and pulleys below, giving
each ankle free motion. Muscles enable the hoofs to pinch
the rocks. They land without hurting themselves because
the hoofs are covered with an elastic material that absorbs the
shock and settles the animal more gently than springs settle a
Cadillac.

Another extraordinary pair of feet is that of the jacana: it
can carry a heavy bird over the precarious tops of lily pads
without tilting them. In the Great Rift Valley of Kenya,
where lagoons are rimmed with papyrus and covered with
water lilies, dwell the lilytrotters or jacanas, a family of birds
found also in the New World Tropics. Almost literally these
birds "walk on water." Snail and arthropod eaters, they run
over the lily pads hunting food and distributing their weight
over a wide area by means of elongated toes and claws. Ten
inches high, chestnut brown with a black crown and eye
stripe, a white neck and cheek patch, the bird has a foot only
slightly shorter than itself. This it handles in a seemingly
awkward manner. Each foot is lifted high. In mid-air the toes
are spread like a parasol, then placed flat on the plants.
Despite the many movements involved, the birds can travel
at great speeds.

An animal whose fins become feet is indeed an odd-animal
collector's item, and upon learning about one, the "walking
catfish," I went to Florida to see it. A native of India and
Eastern and Southeast Asia, the fish was brought to Florida by

tropical-fish dealers, who dumped several into an outdoor pond a few years ago. With no predator, disease, parasite, or environmental hazards to keep its numbers in check, the exotic fish multiplied rapidly and solved the few problems it met by walking. When pools and streams dry up in winter in that land of wet and dry seasons, this catfish simply wiggles ashore, braces itself on its strong pectoral fins and, rocking back and forth, pushes with its tail to "walk" to water-filled canals and rivers. For the trip on land, the fish shifts from gills to elaborate lung-like organs that absorb oxygen directly from the air. This creature cannot even be controlled with poisons. When the Florida Fish and Game Commission tried to kill them with chemicals in the water, the beasts simply went ashore and walked away.

It is the sea mammals, however, that tell me most vividly that despite his brain and inventions man knows little about travel. Once land mammals like ourselves, dolphins and whales have fused the bones of their front toes, wrists, fore and upper arms into sea paddles, some of which are immobile to the shoulder. They have eliminated legs and changed feet into flukes to become the swiftest animals of the sea. Dolphins can maintain sustained speeds of from twenty-six to thirty-three kilometers per hour, while the large rorqual or fin-back whale shoots through the ocean at thirty-seven kilometers per hour, passing ships at sea. Oscillating their bodies and flukes in a vertical plane, flippers functioning as stabilizers, they not only leap into the air, but dive one thousand meters where pressures are in excess of one hundred atmospheres. As they speed down into the black halls of the oceans, their bodies adjust to the pressure. The pulmonary alveoli collapse and compress the air into the bronchi, tracheae, nasal passages, and when very deep, into several accessory air sacs. This dispersal prevents whales and porpoises from getting the "bends," that human affliction deep-sea divers suffer when pressure forces nitrogen into the blood. The coldness of water, also a problem to divers, is of no consequence to whales and porpoises. They have offset its effects with a host of devices. Their metabolic rate is about three times as high as terrestrial animals of the same weight and is one factor that warms them, while the compactness of flippers and flukes affords little surface area from which to lose heat as compared to our legs and arms. Finally insulating blubber constitutes over forty percent of their body weight.

Side swimming was thought to be unique to man until November 1968 when four zoologists from the Steinhart Aquarium, San Francisco, found the champion side swimmer of the globe in the waters of the muddy Indus River near Sukkar, West Pakistan. It is the blind dolphin, called *susu* by the natives. Three of these beautiful animals were caught in throw nets during the night by native fishermen. At dawn they were shown to the American zoologists, who viewed them with awe, for the graceful white porpoises with their slender beaks had not been seen by Western man since Pliny the Elder described them in 75 A.D. Not even he knew that they swam on their sides, for they live in muddy waters where no man, not even the natives, had seen them swimming.

When they were placed in a holding pond, also thick with silt, the four zoologists suspected that the blind river dolphins swam on their backs like the fresh-water dolphins of the Amazon, for after surfacing to breathe they started to roll over, then disappeared. It was not until November 10th that man saw for the first time the side stroke of these mysterious cetaceans. After they had been placed in a clear pool of water, bodies arched, pectoral flippers up and down, they swam on their sides, going in a clockwise direction if they lay on their left sides and counterclockwise when on their right sides. They always held their heads lower than their tails which kept their heads from bobbing and gave their beaks a lateral sweep as they foraged the bottom for catfish and the dead or living river animals that dwell in the muddy bottoms.

Their side swimming was a surprise, and so were their blind eyes, which were mere pin holes in the head. Brief tests satisfied the Americans that the dolphins saw dark and light or the top and bottom of the river, but no objects are visible to them, for the retina is adapted to light gathering rather than image resolving, and the eyes have an extremely small optic nerve. To offset their blindness, the side swimmers beeped constantly at the rate of twenty to fifty pulses a second. Testing to determine if they were ever silent, the men watched and listened through various instruments for a sixteen-hour stretch. The sun arose, shafts of artificial light were shone down on them, objects were placed in their way, but never did the echo locating cease as it does in sea-faring dolphins that see fairly well and can stop sending out signals when their eyes locate objects.

Injured in the throw nets, refusing to eat, the three rare dolphins never made it back to the United States, but their skeletons are being studied at the California Academy of Science in San Francisco and the Museum of Comparative Zoology, Cambridge, Massachusetts.

One other traveler has achieved recognition recently, for it can convert a forward into a backward movement like the hummingbird, but in the resistant medium of water. The fluke *Schistosoma mansohi* is a member of that very low phylum, Platyhelminthes, the earliest phylum where animals are bilateral like ourselves. In one of its larval stages, this creature has a mechanism that drives it forward then backward without slowing down to reverse. About two years ago, three scientists at the Parasitological Institute in Höchst, Germany, astounded by a device unknown to man, not only determined how the animals manage this, but made a model of the tail which may soon be applied to mixing tasks and driving mechanisms in engineering.

The tail has a stem; on the end of it is a fork. When the fluke larva swims backward, the two branches of the fork spread out like an old English T. While swimming forward, the branches close. Depending on how they align with the tail, they can change from forward swimming to backward without significantly altering the stroke rate or their speed. As the fluke larvae change directions, their bodies lengthen and grow more narrow. The entire movement is a whirling, swirling, up and down action that adjusts to any change of direction instantly. This, together with the ability of the animal to make its joints rigid or flexed, long or short, propels the creature in this extraordinary manner. The model called *Cercaria I,* the Latin name for the larval stage of the fluke, has an adjustable forked tail made of rigid material with a joint that is sufficiently adaptable to also produce a forward movement that can be converted into a backward movement and vice versa. Its transverse branches fold with the action of its joint. If ever there is a flying saucer of the sea devised by some intelligence greater than ours, it will come on the tail of the fluke, a device that defies the drag of reversal in water.

Some critics might say that no lower form of life has gone to the moon. But even this is not so; in fact, they have gone us one better. Having hitchhiked there on man-made equipment, some, unlike us, are still up there on the deserted equipment. Bacteria, that tough third life that is neither plant nor animal, are upon the moon right now.

When some of the old hardware was brought down by the crew of Apollo 12, these creatures awakened from their torpor and went on growing on the earth.

Going through the file of the travelers I had collected, I looked down at my own primitive, plantigrade feet and decided that the only way they could compete with the lower animals was to resign them to comfort and put them up before the fire.

# CHAPTER 4

# OF COURTSHIP AND SEX

IT IS the lovers of the earth that are the great experimenters as by ones, twos, or whole communities, animals fulfill their function of renewing the species. To this end, every means under the sun seems possible. Each individual, be it robin, tiger, or snail, has a reproductive system divided into two time scales. One is for the individual. Out of the hereditary code box come rapid chemical signals that set off endocrine or hormonal processes. And the individual is impelled to place his offspring in a suitable environment where they have some chance to survive.

The other time scale is slow. It works for the survival of the race. No rapid feedback of signals from an environment can tell an individual how to ensure the perpetuation of his species over the ages. These adjustments must be made in those mysterious parts of the reproductive system that react through generations upon generations. It took over 75 million years for the camel to change from a small, short-necked, long-tailed herbivore with a straight back in the Paleocene days, to the large, long-necked, short-tailed, humped-back camel adapted to modern plants and modern desert conditions. Over a hundred generations passed before the housefly and other insects became adjusted to DDT.

The duplication of life is initiated by sex, male and female elements of varying degrees of sophistication. Until the last few years it was believed that the very low forms of life were without sex, and that this included the trillions of one-celled animals that infuse the seas, ponds, and streams.

In light of new information an exciting fact stands out. Only one of the hundreds of thousands of classes of animals is sexless, the common amoeba and its kin, the Sarcodines. Even the bacteria, which were thought to be sexless, have male and female parts. Scientists have now seen, through high-powered microscopes, the half-plant, half-animal members of the Third Kingdom, Protista, exchange codes, and exchanging codes is sex.

But the common amoeba and others of its class are the miraculous exceptions. They divide. An individual grows narrower in the middle, and as it does so, internal parts called food vacuoles, nuclei, and others "split" and move toward the ends. Cell walls enclose the parts, sever—and there are two individuals where there was one. Remarkably, each half is younger than the original amoeba and has to grow up in preparation for the next division. These split, perpetuating the original animal in what is described as "apparent immortality." The original amoeba, wherever it is after thousands of splittings, never dies, according to British scientists, if fed an unlimited supply of *Tetrahymena* (a simple plant). When put on a maintenance diet, the animals have a definite life span, grow old, and die.

All other animals and all other classes of Protozoa, it is now known, are sexual. The paramecium of zoology-class fame exchanges sexual codes through the mouth. The Ciliata, another group of one-celled animals, seem sexless, but are not. Two come together, fuse, and while latched each produces a gamete nucleus. This they exchange. The swap results in two zygotes. When this is formed the "parents" separate and the zygotes undergo rapid division, alike elements moving into four different parts of the parent. The four parts divide into four Ciliata, and from the union come eight new creatures.

Although this sounds simple enough, it is vastly complex and I spent an evening with a zoologist trying to understand the sex life of the one-celled animals.

"Amoeba are extraordinary," she said, "but truly remarkable are the Coelenterates." She opened a book. "The hydras, sea anemones, jellyfish, and corals are asexual," she began. "That is, the adults have neither male nor female parts. They bud, an asexual process, but throw off animals that are completely different in appearance and are sexual. These are called medusa. They float through the water and male and female parts combine to make still another animal, the planula. This swims freely about for several hours to days, settles down on the bottom, and becomes another sexless adult." She shook her head. "Miraculous!"

*Whiptail lizard: no males*

Strange as this is, even stranger is the whiptail lizard of the genus *Cnemidophorus*. The rule is that all animals with backbones are heterosexual. However, this slender reptile of our Southwestern deserts is the earth's most astonishing rule breaker. Among these swift-footed lizards there are no males. The females give birth to females who give birth to females who give birth to females, ad infinitum. The process, known as parthenogenesis, sometimes occurs in lower forms of life. Parthenogenesis has also been induced artificially by pricking frog eggs with a needle, and cooling rabbit eggs or treating them with acid. Under such conditions the eggs develop into baby tadpoles and rabbits, some of which have been raised to maturity. They are all females. This by no means explains the whiptail lizard, however, for in nature parthenogenesis is unknown in animals higher on the life scale than the aphid, and even among them there are males on occasion. So unbelievable are the whiptails that a skeptical zoologist, Dr. Paul Maslin of the University of Colorado Museum, captured several females about three years ago and raised them in complete isolation. They bore daughters and their daughters bore daughters for three generations to date. At the last report, these undisputed matriarchs of the wilds were still maintaining their race. Each offspring looks exactly like her mother, a phenomenon of parthenogenesis, and each has proven herself capable of producing more young. Without a doubt the whiptail lizards follow rules of their own.

In no area was I more confused by my file of exceptional beasts than in the ways they have found to beget young. No sooner is there a general principle for some phylum than there is an exception. Most one-celled animals perpetuate their race by either dividing or budding, asexually, but several of these lowly creatures are also sexual. *Volvox*, a protozoa of fresh-water ponds, is a ball-like colony of 500 to 50,000 vegetative cells. It usually buds, but occasionally a colony becomes a female and creates an egg at the rear of the ball. The egg inspires the colony to become loaded with food and to increase in size. Then, as if the egg has some mysterious effect on its kind, a particular cell within that colony or in another nearby gives rise to many small flagellated sperm. The sperm rupture the walls of their home and penetrate the colony where the egg lies. Fertilized, the egg grows, bursts free, and becomes a new colony which reproduces by its more usual method of budding. The sexually conceived *Volvox* is exceptional in its phylum but not so in appearance. Biologists have found it indistinguishable from those produced by budding.

In one phylum higher on the ladder of life there exists an even more astonishing reproductive system—sponges have "matchmakers." This name has been given by zoologists to a cell that literally introduces the sperm to the egg. On rare occasions sponges reproduce not by budding or by bits and pieces regenerating, but sexually like the *Volvox*. Sperm arise within the walls of a sponge colony; whether from one individual or the group no one knows. Scientists know only that, when mature, the sperm wash out through holes in the colony and into the holes in another sponge. No sooner does the male element enter than it is met at the door by the matchmaker, a peculiar cell surrounded by a collar. It encases the sperm, then "rowing" with hairs that grow out from the collar, carries the sperm off through the sponge in search of the egg. Through some incredible sense, it not only locates, but docks on the ova and latches itself there securely. When tightly fused the matchmaker transfers the sperm to the egg and a new sponge begins. How this fabulous little cell—brainless, eyeless—knows which of the billions of organisms passing into a sponge to meet and where to take it to find an egg is one of those mysteries that is locked in animal life, probably to remain there forever.

The sponge colony can afford to risk a rare sperm and egg to a matchmaker, for if this system fails, the sponge can always reproduce by budding or regeneration. In higher and more complicated forms of life where these miraculous tricks are impossible, no matchmaker can be trusted to bring the sperm to the egg. There must be that masculine contribution to the security of the race, the penis, and the female contribution, the vagina or door, and the oviduct or corridor that leads the sperm to the egg. The organs, known by these terms, appear in even lower forms of life, such as the flatworms, a phylum of parasitic flukes and tapeworms and in nonparasitic marine species (Platyhelminthes). Of these the tapeworms have no

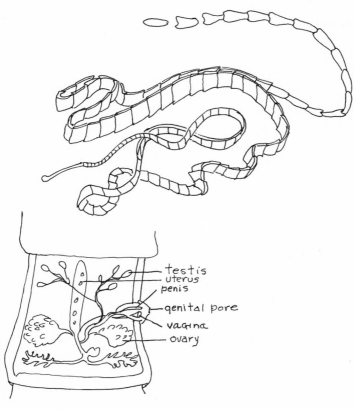

*Tapeworm: hermaphrodite in every segment*

mouths or any trace of a digestive system, but do have highly developed sex organs. Tapeworms live in the intestines of higher animals and simply soak up nourishment. They have heads, short necks or growing regions, and fifty to a hundred sections, each of which contains nothing but reproductive parts—making this animal the most sexual creature of the earth! In each section is a male part of numerous small testes connected to a large sperm duct at the end of which is a modified muscular organ, the penis. Running parallel to the sperm duct in the same segment are the female parts, an oviduct egg and a vagina. Both male and female parts open in the same genital chamber on the outside of the section. Although all the penes can eject sperm and fertilize the female organ in their own section, more often they reach down the line to a more mature female part. To accommodate all the mating sections, the worm folds back on itself, renewing life in the shape of a looped ribbon.

In the phylum above the flatworms, the Nemertina or proboscis worms, the sexes become separated into male and female individuals, with the exception of a few fresh-water forms that have remained hermaphroditic with both male and female parts in one animal like the tapeworm. For the most part, however, from the Nemertina to man, there are "boys" and "girls"—the sexes—who get together and exchange codes in astonishing ways. The American oysters have a community arrangement. Since egg and sperm are joined together by the bouyant water, as in most sea forms including fish, the males have their sex organs on their feet, that muscular disc, which when they open their shells comes in contact with the water first, a practical place for an oyster's code of life to lie.

The mating is not initiated by either male or female, but by the sea itself. Cemented for a lifetime to rock, the oysters wait until the water reaches a certain temperature, about 60° F. along the Eastern coast. In the spring of the year storms may come, the ocean may chill, and waves beat high, so the oysters have set their reproductive clocks to a temperature signal that means the arrival of the calmer and more temperate waters of summer. The temperature reaches the magical degree, the clock goes off, the tide starts out, and one male, usually an old one, starts the ceremony. He opens his shell and sheds his sperm. They drift down the rocky oyster bed and touch other males. These then join in, open their shells, and shed their life codes into the water. When the oyster bed is dense with sperm, the females answer this call of spring, open their shells, and cast their eggs among the sperm. Fertilized, the eggs ride to sea on the exhalant time where far out in the plankton beds they develop and hatch. Resembling tiny peas with streamers, the larvae spin and whirl freely, wild little creatures so different from their parents that no one knew they were oysters until about twenty years ago.

In a week to ten days the baby oysters begin to sink and twirl toward the estuaries and the rocks of home. Millions grow too heavy too soon, drop on mud, and die; others hit the oyster beds head on, exude cement, stick, and live. Within hours these change from free creatures with fringes into glassy replicas of their stolid parents. Their spree over, they remain where they strike for the rest of their lives.

The European oyster reproduces quite differently, oddly enough, while it eats and breathes. As a female takes in food and oxygen through her syphons in spring the sperm ride into her body. Somehow she jets the food to her stomach and the oxygen and sperm to her gills where the eggs lie. After fertilization the eggs rupture and are breathed out through the syphons as gently as the sperm came in.

Males of another member of this phylum, the squid and octopus, carry their code of life to their females on one of the most bizarre contraptions of the animal kingdom—an arm of love. One of the ten arms of the male squid, usually the fourth right or left, is an intromissive organ. On it lies a spoon-like depression or cavity that carries sperm. When the male is ready to mate, he reaches into the sperm sac in his body with this arm and scoops up his precious code. He then sets off to find a female. Upon meeting her, he initiates the ritual of courtship which has one function—to time both individuals for the mating. The dance of the male is joined by the female as both show off their graceful tentacles in rhythmical undulations. At the right moment, the male thrusts his special arm into the female's mantel and leaves his spermatozoa in a pocket near the opening of her oviduct. Then he drifts away.

As in other groups some squids vary their family act. In a few species the arm breaks off and disintegrates, leaving the sperm in the receptacle. The male loligo, on the other hand, mates with a blow to the chin, for the sperm receptacle of his female is located in a fold beneath her mouth. In all, however, sperm are held until the female is ready to lay, which can be days or even weeks later.

Both lyrical and strange to us are courtship and mating in the ever-moving sea; yet under our feet, in our houses and yards, dwell the most rococo lovers of the earth—the spiders. Long admired for the artistry of their webs, the females of this class, the arachnids, are so predatory that for self-protection the males have evolved some of the most elaborate mating rituals of the animal kingdom. Like the octopi and squids, male spiders have a special organ, the pedipalpi or sex feet, on which the male passes sperm to the female. These are situated on each side of the mouth and resemble legs, but have a rounded copulatory organ at the end of each ped. With these a male is able to deliver his code of life and get away before he is killed by the murderous female.

Maturing before the female, the male weaves a small web, the only one he spins. To this he makes love, for he has two courtships, one to himself, which is gentle, and one to a female, which is harassing. Hidden alone among the foliage or close to the ground, he rubs his body against his own web.

Usually after dark (most spiders are nocturnal) as the winds sing and nighthawks fly overhead, the clock of reproduction strikes the hour of this male contribution to spider life and sperm falls on the web. Placing his pedipalpi in this fluid he absorbs it—a process that takes one to four hours, depending on the species and that excites him to tremble and quiver. Then he sets out on the dangerous mission of delivering his code to a female.

The female helps in only one way; she has evolved a shoe for his foot, a pocket that lies in front of her genital opening. Here the sperm is stored until she is ready to lay eggs. However it lies below her poison-filled fangs, which strike without distinction, and so the males of each species have countered this in one way or another to reach the receptacle alive.

Most male spiders are much smaller than their female counterparts for at least one good reason—to make the approach unnoticeably. The male *Nephila,* an orb-weaving spider of the tropics, weighs a thousand times less than his mate and is so nondescript that he can crawl upon her, come down and around her, and leave his sperm in her pocket without attracting her attention.

The beautiful black and orange garden spider male has no such advantage (being only slightly smaller than she), so he has invented a long-distance telegraphing system to woo her before approaching. Taking one of her web strands in his foot, he snaps it to announce his species and sex. Legs poised for flight, he waits. If there is no answer on the line or if it trembles with the footsteps of an attacking female, he drops to the ground and darts off. If, however, the female is receptive, he will receive a gentle answer to his inquiry. A second courtship begins. Tugging gently on her line he subdues her with spider messages and eventually sneaks up to her. Then he calms her by stroking her with his foot until she is tranquilized sufficiently for him to place his feet in her shoe, deposit the sperm, and make his getaway.

The courtship of the male tarantula is more dramatic and dangerous. Having made love to his web, he destroys it, then wanders into the night desert, touching everything he encounters in the hope of finding a mate (he cannot see well). On a field trip one night in the Arizona-Sonoran Desert near Tucson, Mr. William Woodin, Director of the Desert Museum, demonstrated this by tapping his fingers on the ground near a prowling male. The furry beast, so big that it looked something like a hand itself running along on its fingers, paused and ran up the human hand before him, then sensing that this was not a female tarantula, scurried down and into the dark. Such is the sex drive of the tarantula and such is the courage of scientific investigation.

Somewhere, perhaps that night, this male would eventually touch a female tarantula, if only her foot or a hair. Before she could kill he would turn on her and beat his four front feet against a leg or on her body. She would rear to attack, fangs open to strike. The male would then clutch her deadly fangs with special hooks on his front legs and, holding her securely, drum on her abdomen with his sex feet. If she is quieted by this pummeling (some are not), he then slips his feet into her shoe. Withdrawing his pedipalpi, he swaggers slowly into the dark, for the tarantula female does not attack after mating.

Males of another family of spiders, the Gnaphoids, tie their females down to avoid being killed. One of these is familiar to almost everyone, the little gray-brown house spider, the males of which wait in the corners of rooms and cupboards until a nearby female has shed her final skin (as spiders grow to maturity, they shed their outgrown skin). Now she is as weak as a soft-shelled crab. He grabs her, wraps her securely in silk, and puts his pedipalpi in her pocket. I found such a female who had been tied for insemination to the drain of the bathroom sink last fall. I wouldn't let visitors or my children wash their hands until the female's chitin had hardened and I could see her emerge. She awoke like a sleeping beauty, threw back her shroud, swept out of the sink, and let herself down to the floor. The next day she was back on her web in a corner.

Given the dangerous mission of mating and given the ability to spin, there is bound to be one spider that would literally have to lasso a mate. And so there is, the *Xysticus* or crab spider, a stubby small species. You can find the females hiding in the petals of flowers anywhere in the United States, waiting to seize insects that come to the blossoms. When not hunting, they are often traveling on the ground, and it is here they are roped by the clever males. Upon seeing a female, the male throws a line, catches her foot, and anchors it to the ground. Then lassoing another foot and another, he ties all eight of them down. As if that were not enough, he spins lines

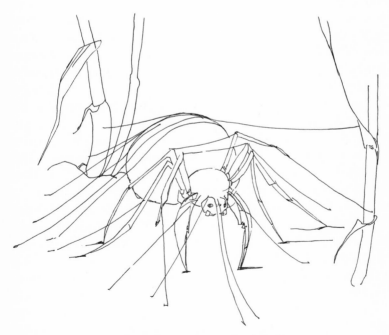

*Crab spider—the female tied down*

across her abdomen, back, and head to shroud her in a "bridal veil" from which she cannot escape.

Insects are the six-legged members of the phylum Arthropoda—that phylum that includes spiders and crustaceans, such as crabs and barnacles. Like the spiders, insects place their spermatozoa in a female receptacle where they are stored until egg laying time. The egg or ovum passes down the oviduct where a shell is put on *before* fertilization; reptiles and birds shed an egg after it is fertilized. For the entrance of the insect sperm, a tiny pore is left in each egg, which is then sealed mysteriously.

Among the insects no creature proves more vividly than the honey bee that the reproductive system works toward strong and healthy progeny. The queen, or reproductive part of the hive, puts a male to such a severe test that only the most durable is able to pass on his code. A queen bee, upon hatching from her large cell where she has received a special food of sexual growth called "royal honey," grows wings, matures, and one day hums through the corridors of the hive piping a call to the drones, who have only one duty in life—to mate. They arise from their lethargy and follow her across the glistening honey combs to the door.

Her suitors at her heels, the virgin queen spreads her wings and takes off for the sky. She climbs out of sight, going higher and higher to eliminate the weak drones, who drop dead from exertion. The strong climb on. Just how high the queen goes is not known, but she goes high enough to eliminate all but one (and sometimes all). Somewhere above earth she mates with her drone in a violent act that shatters his wings and body and tears his legs apart. Her mate scattered across the terrain, she returns to the hive door with enough sperm to last her lifetime of egglaying—ten to twelve years.

Keeper of her race, the supreme decision maker for her line, the queen bee is not unique in her choice of a mate. All mankind can understand a female who selects a male for power and vigor. But what of a female who switches her sex to mate with another female? It happens.

There dwells in the warm Mexican waters a female fish, *Xiphophorus,* a swordtail, who for part of her life follows the wisdom of her sex and mates with a male. As time passes and she grows older, an eerie change overtakes her reproductive system; she travels to the breeding grounds not to mate with a male, but to switch her sex and throw sperm on the eggs of younger females.

Perhaps the reason for this incredible phenomenon can be attributed to the male. As his Latin name implies, *Xiphophorus* is a "double monster." His sex organ is a modified anal fin that has several enlarged rays with hook-like projections. Vicious and injurious, this organ might possibly explain why these females have been forced to abandon sex and invent a gentler method for fertilizing eggs. As a scientist friend of mine said of this fish: "That's the best of all possible worlds— to know what it is to be mother *and* father."

Another extraordinary sex life has been developed by the eel. Both the European and American eel are born in the Sargasso Sea, a vast area of the Atlantic Ocean marked by heavy growth of seaweed some two thousand miles west of the Canary Islands. By yet unknown guideposts, the European eels catch the North Equatorial Current and are carried on a two-year trip to European shores. The American eels, without exception, ride the Gulf Stream and come north to the United States in one year. While traveling both eels are in a larval stage that looks more like willow leaves than fish or even eels. Precisely upon arriving at the mouths of fresh-water rivers, the leaves change into little thread-like eels or elvers. Leaping, swimming, wriggling, they work their way from the river mouths to the streams, from the streams to lakes and ponds, a journey that takes them about three years. During this time they are sexless. Neither male nor female organs are present in their bodies, a mystery that led early scientists to believe

that eels must reproduce by spontaneous generation—a mythi-
cal process by which the young burst into life from inert mud,
not from eggs.

Not until the twentieth century did scientists discover how
eels reproduce. When several years old and about three feet
long, they turn around by the dark of the August moon and
head back to the sea. They no longer eat, but swirl around
rocks, down streams and rivers, back to the brackish waters
near the sea.

Here individuals become both male and female, as
each develops both ovaries and testes of equal maturity. As
hermaphrodites, they wait for some mysterious signal to tell
them whether to become male or female. A few scientists believe that the dominant sex is already there, that despite the
presence of ovaries and testes, each individual is destined in
time to become one sex or the other. Another theory is that
the signal to become one sex or the other is set by the environment. A group of eels, locked in a basin near the coast of France
from which they could not migrate, all turned into females,
as if by chance one male might retrieve the species from
oblivion. On the other hand, eels planted in the Great Lakes
and also restrained from reaching their destination in the
Sargasso Sea remained sexless for ten to twelve years. No one
knows what determines the sex of an eel, but each spring
another host of elvers arrives at the mouth of the rivers.

That the environment can inform the tissues of a beast
how to adjust sex to its home conditions becomes brilliantly
clear in reproductive habits of the fabulous angler fish. A
creature of the dark ocean deeps where life is scattered widely,
the angler fish has become a Christmas tree of adaptations.
It has modified its dorsal fin into a fishing rod. From the rod
grows a "fishing" line, and on the end of that line is a lure
that moves like bait to attract the rare victim that passes by.
In addition, phosphorescent organs on the body light up the
angler, perhaps to induce some swimmer to come curiously

toward the light, see the lure, approach, and become food for the angler.

To overcome the problem of mating in an environment so sparsely inhabited, the angler has turned to a method even more fantastic than its food gathering. Shortly after the eggs are hatched in that black world at the bottom of the ocean, the male angler, through some instinct, catches a female before she is separated from him, possibly for a lifetime. He does this by hitting her throat, back, or side, sinking in his jaws, and never letting go again. What happens next defies all laws except those of reproduction. As time passes and the two move through the dark abyss, the skin of the growing female spreads over the male, her blood vessels connect with his, his mouth disappears, and he becomes a small sex appendage with only one purpose in life—to fertilize the eggs of his hostess. Such a preposterous pair can be seen at the Hall of Fishes in the American Museum of Natural History in New York, where a female angler and her consort, caught off the coast

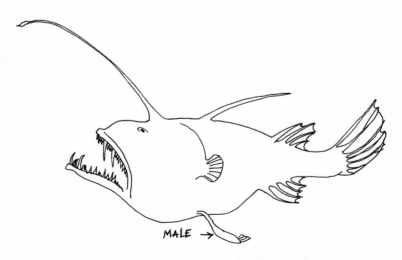

MALE →

*Lonely angler fish, with built-in male*

of England, are displayed for all to ponder the insistence of the reproduction system and the plight or delight of a male that is stuck to his wife forever.

Male reptiles—snakes, lizards, alligators, and turtles—ensure the continuance of their race with their own invention, two penes that have been named as if one, the hemipenis. This or these lie near the vent and only one is used during mating. In most reptilian species, these penes are covered with numerous sharp spines and so must unfold inside out during copulation. This is done by an extraordinary mechanism, a muscle that is attached to the tip of the hemipenis and that pulls it down and out of the sheath and tail.

Although we rarely think of reptiles as affectionate, during courtship a few seem almost tender. The large anacondas and boa constrictors have tiny vestigial legs with which they softly scratch their mates, and our water and garter snakes court with a gentle touch, as the male rubs his chin across the female's back.

The familiar box turtle of our woods and forests courts by knocking politely. Around four o'clock on a June afternoon a male turtle will approach a female and tap on her shell with his belly plates. When she answers by doing nothing, he keeps on knocking until she is receptive and ready to permit him to climb awkwardly onto her back, a position that releases the hemipenis, one of which finds its way into her vagina. According to records, she always deposits her eggs in the six o'clock twilight, covers them with earth, and walks away.

Since snakes and turtles have double penes, the thought occurred to me that perhaps there were females somewhere on this earth with two reproductive tracts. I rejected the idea as too preposterous even from the ingenious animals, only to find recently among the records of the American Society of Mammalogists that this is indeed so. Female oppossums, kangaroos, wombats, and bandicoots (to name a few of the marsupials) have double vaginas and uteri! I searched the scientific literature for some explanation of this, but the anatomists of these primitive mammals simply state "vagina and uterus bifurcated," together with the tantalizing statement that the male's penis is forked.

The anatomy of these females raises many unanswerable questions, one of which is whether or not the mothers have two pregnancies at the same time. As far as the wombat and several species of kangaroos are concerned, the answer is clear. They give birth to one baby, very rarely two. As for other marsupials, the oppossum bears ten to twenty-five young. If both uteri become pregnant at the same time, nature has taken care of what may seem to a woman to be a primary problem—the burden of it all. Marsupials do not have bulky placentas, the food supply to their young being provided largely by the yolk, like a bird rather than a mammal. And, of course, the young are mere embryos at birth when they enter the pouch.

The continuance of life among birds reaches wondrous heights not only in their spectacular courtship displays but in the sexual act as well. Both male and female have what is known as a cloaca, that opening under the tail familiar to anyone who prepares a chicken or a turkey for the table. It serves not only as a reproductive organ, but as an outlet for body wastes. Birds evolved from the fishes via the reptiles and, like them, have but one opening. Unlike fish, however, they have no water environment to carry the sperm to the egg, nor do the males have an intromittant organ or penis, as in reptiles and mammals. Yet in less than one second the swifts mate on the wing, the warblers on twigs, the pheasants on the ground.

Most wild birds mate but once a day during the breeding season, but the little house sparrow of city streets and country yards is an exception. An ornithologist at the University of Michigan counted fourteen successive matings of a pair that were nesting on the sill outside his laboratory window.

Courtship not only serves to bring the pair of birds together, but also starts the egg on its journey down the oviduct and awakens the glands that put layers of yolk, albumen, and shell upon the ova. Niko Tinbergen, the bird behaviorist of Oxford, England, has observed that courtship also serves to suppress tendencies of aggression or escape. For most of us, however, the courtship of birds is the poetry of spring as songs fill the dawn and feathers shine with color. We see the red-winged blackbird flash his orange and red shoulder patches and the woodcock, calling from heights beyond our sight, dive toward earth, wings whistling. Such scenes are familiar to bird lovers. Preceding this, however, is another bird ceremony known as pair formation. The male black-crowned night heron is the king of this courtly behavior. Upon his return to breeding grounds that extend from Florida and the Gulf of Mexico to Quebec, he selects a territory and a nest on which to stand with a stick in his bill. Loudly he snaps his beak on the stick while moving his head rhythmically up and down. Should this fail to lure a mate he will take two or three steps forward, halt, arch his back, lower his head until his bill is almost down to his feet, and, while raising one foot, produce a cluck in his throat that is followed by a prolonged and audible hiss. This he repeats until a female alights beside him.

After pairing, courtship among birds becomes a varied display. The male American coot builds a reed platform of sticks on which to strut and court. The male Australian zebra finch twirls on the end of a twig, singing as he dances. His crown feathers pulled down trimly, his white belly and spotted flank feathers puffed out, he twists his tail until the black and white bands on the upper tail coverts are turned toward the female. This inspires her to lower her body in a horizontal plane and rapidly vibrate her tail, a signal of acceptance.

The great frigatebird of the Pacific and South Atlantic islets opens his wings and rocks to and fro as he inflates a red throat to the size of a toy balloon. He then trumpets in a voice so powerful it fairly rocks the island trees.

Even noisier is the courtship of the Adélie penguin, which begins when one of the pair brings a stone to the nest. The male will slowly stretch his head up, beat his flippers, and throw out his chest, then looking proud and pompous, he emits a drum roll of sounds that can be heard half a mile away. With this, the female faces him and together they point their bills up, roll their eyes down and back, raise their crests, press their flippers to their sides, and sway to the accompaniment of thundering calls.

It is the male bowerbirds of Australia and New Guinea, however, that are the Don Juans of the earth. Just for courtship and mating (not home building) these birds erect structures so intricate that early explorers thought they were homes of natives.

Some make "stages," some decorate "maypoles," and a third group lays out "avenues." Of the stage builders, the Sanford's golden-crested bowerbird is the most imaginative. He builds a circus ring on the mossy floor of a palm forest and decorates its edges with the sparkling wings of beetles, the subtly colored shells of snails, and chunks of resin. Around his treasures he hangs a curtain of bamboo sticks and fern leaves from vines above. Behinds this he rearranges his jewels or poses each day, flexing his body like a weight lifter before a camera. The love bower prepared, he then hops around his ring singing as gloriously as a mockingbird until his mate is lured to his rendezvous. Within its walls, his poses together with the sight of his exquisite collection readies the female, and they copulate behind the curtain.

The Maypole builder of renown is the golden bowerbird. But nine inches long, he builds around a sapling a cone of sticks that, with additions yearly, may tower to the incredible height of nine feet. Nearby is another "house," a coned roof walled gracefully with vines. The large structure is to attract

*Regent bowerbird, painting his corridor*

the female, the smaller one is for copulation. In this delicate bedroom the male places orchids, bright flowers, lacy mosses, and ferns, offset with neat piles of shells and berries. He decorates with a sense of beauty that is comparable to our own, even to replacing wilted flowers with fresh ones.

The avenue builders exceed the Maypole builders in both engineering and art. The male clears a space four feet in diameter and floors it with sticks. He then erects two closely parallel walls of twigs by driving them into the ground with his beak and binding them together with bits of vine and plant fiber. Making the passage just wide enough for him to walk through without hitting his wings, he covers the narrow floor with bleached bones, flowers, and colorful pebbles. You would think that he could achieve no more, yet he does—he paints the walls with plant juices and a twig brush!

The regent bowerbird, who is navy blue with gold head and wing patches, mixes earth colors with plant pigments, charcoal, and saliva for paint. He dips wadded leaf or bark into this and daubs the walls of his avenues until they glow gray-blue or green. The floor is strewn with glittering objects. Then he sings in a guttural voice, calling his mate to come see his paintings above jewel-bedecked floors.

After mating, all the male bowerbirds, having achieved their creative goals, take no further part in reproductive duties. The females go off by themselves to build shallow cup-like nests of twigs, and they alone rear the young. But what female would object after being presented the treasures of the jungle and the creative paintings of a male in a castle he himself built for their union?

A male bird of paradise named Wallace's standard-wing is considered by ornithologists to be the finest lover in appearance and dance. From his wings grow four creamy plumes, like long slender teardrops, which he lifts as he spreads a triangle of iridescent green and gold feathers that shimmer like metal under his chin. Gloriously displayed, feathers spread, he slowly stretches upward, trembling as if in a fit. At the height of the reach he flips over backwards in a rocket of color and lands on his feet with closed wings.

Compared to the bright love acrobatics of birds, mammals seem dull, for they are secretive in courtship and sex in accordance with their way of life.

The highest form of life, mammals insure the perpetuation of their race in the most protective ways. The testes of many rodents, bats, and insectivores are buried safely within the body, descending into an external sac only during the breeding season, for most mammalian sperm can survive only if cooler than the body. But marine mammals and anteaters retain the testes within the body at all times. Among the hoofed animals, sheep, cattle, deer and others, the testes lie within the external scrotum and are located behind the penis. In the marsupials, however, such as the kangaroos of Australia and the opossums of North America, the scrotum is in front of the penis, a primitive position that evolution seems to have revised and improved in the more sophisticated mammals.

Mammalian sperm and eggs are rare compared to the lavish numbers of the oyster, so to ensure the continuance of life, the male carnivores, dogs, primates, bats and a few insectivores have developed a bone or "os penis." It lies within the male copulatory organ and seems to "lock" the pair together until fertilization is accomplished. However, no scientist truly understands the function of this unusual bone.

The mammalian female, for her part, holds ovaries in her body—small flattened organs that house tiny eggs—as microscopic in a mouse as in a whale. She also protects them with the most elaborate of devices, the endocrine system of the female mammal. When liberated, the egg enters the Fallopian tubes where it is fertilized and then travels to the uterus. It is then implanted in the uterine wall, an act that continues the magical hormonal interaction, a perfectly timed series of bodily events programmed for the growth and survival of the embryo and fetus. Below the uterus, ducts and tubes unite to form the vagina, at the ventral end of which lies a small sense organ called the clitoris. An exception occurs in the female spider monkey of Southern Mexico and Bolivia. So large and protruding is the clitoris of this species that collectors have captured females believing them to be males.

Because of the rarity of mammalian eggs, ovulation is restricted to a definite period known as oestrum or "heat," and if penetration occurs at this time, pregnancy normally follows. This occurs but once a year in foxes, bears, seals, and many other mammals, while the more vulnerable shrews, tree squirrels, and mice ovulate frequently to replace their losses. So preyed upon is the white-footed deer mouse, that upon giving birth she immediately mates again.

Unaware of this, I was alarmed for the well-being of a mouse I was raising in a Michigan study camp. After giving birth to eight pink babies, she cleaned and tucked them into her belly fur. At that moment, up from under the floor of the tent came a male who ran across my foot, wedged himself through the loosely latched cage door, and jumped on the female. I attempted to remove him to protect the family, only to be bitten by the enraged female whose reproductive time clock was already set to replace her offspring. In her native woods probably only one of her brood would live to maturity.

The preyed upon have another way to assure their continuance. For most mammals, fertilization requires but one mating, but mice mate from sixty-five to seventy-five times in a session, and Shaw's jird, a rodent of Israel, was observed to have mated 224 times in two hours.

Large litters also ensure the continuance of vulnerable mammal species. The female tenrec or tenreecid surpasses all other mammals in this area. Thirty-two embryos were found in the body of one of these primitive insect eaters of the African forest.

People appear to be most curious about the courtship and mating of the porcupine. I approached a Michigan mammalologist to see if he could clear up the mystery. The answer is very simple—the porcupine male is the only terrestrial mammal that does not grasp his female; they come together without touching quills. Furthermore, he has a rapid muscular rather than vascular penial erection (two to four seconds). And they do not mate often.

All lower mammals, with the exception of the two-toed sloth (who mates front to front) hold the female from behind, even while hanging by their feet (as do the flying foxes and large fruit-eating bats of the Old World from Africa to

Australia) or while moving through the water (as does the duck-billed platypus). This playful male takes the tail of his female in his bill and, in an act of courtship, swims in circles with her until she is receptive.

Although the time of ovulation is usually determined by the female, in a few rare cases it is sparked by the male in a process when he copulates. The entrance of the male organ into the female signals the deeply buried eggs to erupt and start down the oviduct. The male hedgehog of Eurasia, Africa, Ceylon, and Madagascar and the males of our own common bat, cats, and rabbits have this unique gift to summon the egg. And our bat, that seemingly unpretentious little fellow of attics and belfries, can do this hanging upside down.

In jungle treetops, communal lovemaking is part of the natural social order among several species of monkey, the most noted of which are the attractive little rhesus and the vocal howling monkeys. Females will accept any male who will have them without arousing jealousy or aggression among other males or females. Dr. C. R. Carpenter, anthropologist-primatologist of the University of Georgia, studied a group of these monkeys on Santiago Island, Puerto Rico, several years ago and never saw a male behave aggressively toward the female during the sex act, nor did he observe any vigorous competition among the males for a female. The females initiate the act, and if one male is not in the mood she will approach another. The mating arouses about as much attention as one monkey grooming another and not nearly as much as a newborn baby, which is viewed with excitement. After fertilization, a process that takes several days to a week and numerous males and matings, the females move into a group of mothers and young and await the arrival of their babies.

Gibbons also are relaxed in their sexual relations, Carpenter found. The center of their social life is a mature pair who form the core of a group. A maturing male in this society will mate with a sister or half-sister and even with his mother should the father somehow be eliminated. The adolescents are often incited to leave home, the primatologist said, for two reasons: frustration within the home group and the heightened drive of sexual maturity. In this transitional social and biological state, the young males and females wander in groups until they can move from their own into another family.

Among the birds and beasts all manner of social sexual relationships exists; polygamy (a male with a harem), polyandry (a female with several males), and of course monogamy (one male and one female who remain faithful at least for a breeding season and often for life). Rape was believed for years to be a peculiarity of the human species. However, it has now been noted among birds, particularly ducks. Ornithologist R. I. Smith observed that a number of males of the pintail duck of North America, *Anas acuta,* will occasionally pursue one female in a wild chase that often ends in promiscuous copulation which he terms rape. The female is literally attacked. Smith assumed that the act must play an important part in fertilization, but it was not until 1969 that there was indisputable proof of rape. A female Chinese goose produced a gosling with obvious Canada goose parentage. Even so, such evidence in the wilds is difficult to obtain.

Since sparrows often chase a single female in the manner of the pintails, A. S. Cheke of the University of Oxford proved "rape" for these birds through an ingenious experiment. In 1966 he exchanged a clutch of house sparrow with a clutch of tree sparrow eggs. The foster parents raised them and, birds being birds, the young were imprinted on their strange parents. Cheke banded all the young and they were allowed to fledge normally. The following spring he found one of the male house sparrows nesting with a female tree sparrow. When their eggs hatched the male house sparrow fed the young, an act that indicated he was their father. No other male appeared at the nest, but when the little sparrows were fifteen days old

and feathered well enough to be identified, Cheke discovered
that two were hybrids, which belonged to the house sparrow,
but three were pure-bred tree sparrows. The pair raised
another brood, two of which were tree sparrows and two
hybrids. The only male observed feeding them was the male
house sparrow. The evidence was clear, however—the female
had been fertilized by two separate males, one of whom, her
own kind, apparently swept down upon her and departed.
The young birds, detailed plumage notes, and color slides at
all stages of development are in the British Museum in
London, where Cheke deposited them for other students of
bird behavior to study.

Just as I thought I had completed my collection of unique
lovers among animal kind, the entomologist Dr. Theodore H.
Savory described the most bizarre of them all—the false scorpions, members of the class Arachnida. They are crab-like
insects with ten legs, two of which resemble crab's claws, and
they walk with dignity forward and go like lightning backward. They eat spiders, mites, and springtails. Two thousand
species strong, they can be found by sifting handsful of fallen
leaves from any woodland onto newspaper, and they can be
raised on moist blotting paper for observation of the maddest
of all courtships and matings.

The male, upon finding a female, approaches her, shakes
his abdomen, and waves his claws. If she moves toward him
he stops, steps closer, and finally touches her with his forelegs.
With that he lowers his body to the ground, lifts it, and draws
out a vertical thread from his genital opening. He breaks it
off and it stands between them like a little pillar. When it
hardens, the male puts his drop of seminal fluid on its top,
then backs away and waves his claws. The female moves
forward. The pillar enters her body. Instantly the male grabs
her and shakes her so violently that the sperm fall off the
pillar and remain within her body. Nothing in all my notes
matched that for originality.

Given the importance of reproduction, there would also have to be, on this earth, an adult devoted only to sex, and so there is—the beautiful *Ephermerida,* the Mayfly. The male lives but one to two hours to mate and then die. In the spring and early summer, up from the cool brooks and streams all over the world come the nymphs of the Mayflies. They shed their coats and change into young adults with wings just big enough to carry them to the undersides of the leaves near the water. Here they split out of their subimago coats and become mature adults, soft brown in color and adorned with glistening transparent wings and long graceful tail filiplumes.

They do not eat, nor can they, for their mouths are functionless. They can barely even walk, their legs are weak, so they wait in shade until twilight when they take to their new strong wings by the thousands and dance over the water. Up into the air they fly and down to the surface of the water they drop, their filiplumes flowing. Some climb as high as thirty feet where they throw up the tails as brakes and fall swiftly again. The majority of the many thousands of the dancers are males, a preponderance that assures the fertilization of but a dozen or so females. In about two hours the males have completed their only purpose as adults, and dying by the thousands they fall on the water or the leaves of the forest floor in deep glittering piles.

When the dance is done, the males dead, the females return to the water to fight their way through the surface film. Wings wrapped around their abdomens, they creep down a stone until they find a suitable place for their eggs. Bracing legs firmly, bending their tail filaments up, they swing their abdomens from side to side, and each stroke deposits a line of minute eggs.

The survival of the race ensured, they too drop dead.

# CHAPTER 5

# WONDERFUL HOMES

IN SPRING around the earth, wherever the sun's rays begin to fall more directly on one latitude than another and daylight lingers longer, animals both usual and unusual are impelled by their reproductive system to go in search of an environment suitable for their offspring.

When they do, the materials of land and sea are transformed. Nests are shaped, dens are dug, temperatures are tested for suitable waters. Everywhere structures appear, as each parent prepares for its infants. Few places are overlooked, from thawing tundra to heated desert. A mere tree becomes a scaffolding for nests, its hollows a cave, its limbs a nursery, and from its heartwood to its bark every layer is an insect crib. In the fields leaves cradle eggs, roots hide larvae, and buds sustain youngsters, as billions of wild life place trillions of young in their niches where they have the best chance to survive.

A home can be as unsubstantial as the minerals of ocean water on which one-celled plants feed and in turn provide food for vast numbers of sea infants. These, of course, are the plankton beds that in the North Atlantic lie in the North, Baltic, Norwegian, and Greenland seas. The waters of Newfoundland also provide rich "prairies" of plants on which small animals graze and are fed upon by the larvae and adults of higher forms of life—shrimp, barnacles, oysters, and fish. Each of these plankton beds is different from another, having, like a land ecosystem, its own species of plant and animal life that have adapted to its conditions and climate. Each has well defined limits: the curtain of cold water near land, the depth of one hundred fathoms, and the lack of sunlight that the one-celled plants require for the manufacture of starches and sugars.

Within these walls the inhabitants live in layers like dwellers in an apartment house. Over the eons each species has defined itself by adjusting to the specific intensity of light that determines its own floor. As the sun goes down, the animals follow their thresholds to the surface, then sink down again at dawn in a daily rhythm that breathes with the sun.

Permanent residents of the plankton bed such as krill— tiny lobster-like animals—live out their lives in these realms, while others like the oyster larvae remain only a short time before moving back to shore to take up the coastal life of their parents.

It is not a rarity for the young themselves to "build" their homes, some of which are astonishingly complex. Such a home builder is the young of the caddisfly whose parents dwell along the edges of lakes and in quiet shaded waters the world over. Moth-like, but even more delicate, the adults fold soft brown or gray wings like tents above their backs and do not venture far from the water. Inactive during the day, they fly at night and lay their eggs on rocks.

The young hatch and creep to the bottom of a lake or stream seeking the sparkling granules of stone. The larva seizes a tiny pebble with the draghook on its tail, picks up another in its feet, and, spitting animal glue on it, sticks it to the keystone. Cementing stone upon stone, it creates a silo that covers its abdomen but leaves its head and feet free for eating and walking. By adding to the structure as it grows, some species eventually build an inch-long house, beautifully

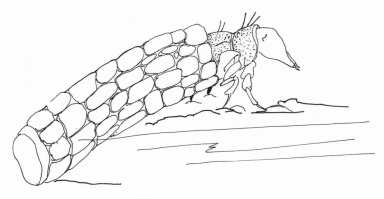

*Caddisfly larva in his silo*

aligned into a cylinder. The tiny animals have an innate knowledge of engineering, and within the stone structure they leave a canal through which water, pumped by tiny hairs, flows to the gills. The canal is formed by placing the stones against three tubercles that grow out of the abdomen.

Before becoming an adult, the caddisfly, like the butterfly, goes into a pupal or cocoon stage, a period of sleep and change. When this time arrives, most of the larvae select a stone with which to block their door. A few, however, cement themselves to a rock, and others spin a silken screen across the entrance. In these beautiful little buildings they transform into flies.

The leaf rollers are another group of home-building young. Silk-producing worms, they shape leaves into tubes and pipes by sitting in the middle of a leaf and throwing threads. If the leaf is to be rolled from the sides, the worm tosses its lines to the edges; if it is to be rolled lengthwise, the larva throws out lines perpendicular to the midrib. As they dry, the strands shrink and pull the edges inward. The larva then throws shorter and shorter strands, the leaf curls around its body, and it is encased in a paper-like house that looks as if it had been formed around a pencil. The roll is then stitched and sealed with webbing. The fascination of this structure is that the caterpillar never exerts pressure on the leaf, but simply lets the shrinkage of the silk construct the home.

There are also leaf tyers, caterpillars that sew the edges of two leaves together, and one—the silver-spotted skipper—creates perhaps the most private home of the animal kingdom. It stitches the five parts of two compound locust leaves together, every edge meeting the other to make a house of many retreats. I have often opened such a leaf and peered into the shadowy castle to find not only the five rooms but the floors matted with silver wall-to-wall carpeting. In one of the rooms lies the caterpillar, and on a memorable occasion I found the little creature with its coat split down the back as it undressed in privacy for the sleep of pupation.

Silk moths have long perplexed me because their cocoons are so tough and their bodies so soft when they emerge that it seemed impossible for them to escape from their tombs. Yet just before emerging a neat round opening appears. In 1967 Drs. Kafatos and Williams of Harvard discovered their secret. The sleepers excrete a remarkable enzyme for the sole purpose of digesting the silk and releasing the adult from its tomb. The Harvard team studied the genus *Antheraea* and noted that about two days before molting the moths exude highly concentrated drops of cocoonase from the skin cells of their otherwise functionless mouth parts. This proenzyme dries into semi-crystals that, when dissolved by another secretion, start off the action that opens their doors to world. More interested in evolution than in how a moth gets out of its cocoon, the chemists found that cocoonase is similar to trypsin, a substance secreted by the pancreas of mammals. This fact supports the hypothesis that mammal and insect proteins have a common origin.

Parents that provide homes for their young make use of every possible and seemingly impossible niche on earth. A fish that places its eggs on the land hardly seems to obey the laws of survival for its kind, but somehow the forces of predation in the sea or some mysterious environmental pull carries the grunion of California ashore at egg-laying time. They ride to land with a knowledge of the waves and tides that ocean-ographers envy.

Every two weeks in the spring of the year when the moon pulls the flood tides high upon the beaches, the grunions move into the breakers near land. Fanning and sculling, they wait for the precise moment before the tide has reached its crest, then catch a wave and ride to shore by the thousands. They ride high up the beach, where quickly, while the wave is rushing out, the females drill holes in the sand with their tails, and pour in their eggs while a grounded male flops beside the issuing milt. The females swish their tails to cover the eggs, the whole process taking sixty seconds. The next wave carries them back to sea. The following wave cannot wet them—the tide has turned.

For two weeks the waves do not wet the fertilized eggs in their alien home high up the beaches, but the young develop until the moon raises another flood tide. Then they hatch, struggle for seconds, and are able to swim just as the flood tide returns. At the appointed hour, the young are washed from their suffocating traps and carried out to sea on the foamy waves.

Animals of the oceans find many curious nesting places. The most disquieting is the nest of the female seahorse, a pocket in the belly of the male. Here she lays her eggs, then darts off leaving him to carry the young, his belly extending as they grow. At hatching time he forces open his pouch and, with strong convulsive movements, jets his young into the sea in a parade of tiny ponies.

The fragile eggs of birds are housed in architectural re-ceptacles for offspring that are the most notable in the animal kingdom. With no tools but a beak, from materials that any gust might carry away, birds construct nests that endure rain and wind, conserve heat, and cradle lively youngsters from hours to four and a half months for the silver-cheeked hornbill and over a year for the wandering albatross.

One, however, depends only on itself for nesting material —the Indo-China swiftlet (of the famed bird nest soup) which weaves a nest of saliva. As the mating season nears, the salivary glands under the tongue of the female begin to swell until by nest-building time they are enormously extended. On the wall of a cave she presses her beak on the rock, and, more like a spider than a bird, releases a font of crystal fluid that she weaves by whipping her body back and forth. This hardens into a fragile nest of glass-like lace, a delicate saucer fashioned for eggs.

Other swifts, such as the chimney swifts of North America, also use this fluid drawn from under their tongues to cement sticks to walls, but the tree swift of the Orient seems to have created a problem for herself by building a nest so delicate and small that she cannot sit on it. Lacing together bark, feathers, and saliva on a horizontal limb, she builds a tiny fragile receptacle designed like an acorn cup, only an inch wide and less than an eighth of an inch thick; it holds but one egg. Unable to sit on such a fragile creation without breaking it, she places one foot on each side, puffs out her feathers, and incubates standing on her short legs.

Plants form the basis of the majority of nests. Birds unravel fibrous stems and seek roots, lichens, ferns, mosses, stems, seed down, and flowers as they utilize every possible part of our flora in their homes.

A nest site fascinating for being so original is the vertical rib of a drooping palm frond, on which the palm swift of Africa builds what seems to be an incredible disaster of bird architecture. To the vertical rib, the swift, using saliva, pastes

*Palm swift with glued eggs*

plant floss and feathers to form a nest with a bottom that is narrower than the long axis of the eggs. To solve this additional problem the female turns her two eggs on their small ends and glues them to the nest! Next she has to adjust to the entire oddity by incubating in a vertical position. Through this whole troublesome arrangement, she manages to bring young into the world.

In the northeastern United States, the Baltimore oriole creates the most beautiful of all woven nests from the fibers of the orange milkweed and grapevines—an intricate hanging basket. I had the rare opportunity one spring to watch a female oriole weave her remarkable nest from the first thread to the last. Around 8 A.M. on a May morning, a gold-breasted, brown-backed oriole female alighted on an orange milkweed plant near the woods and, fluttering her wings and jerking her head, stripped off an almost invisible thread and carried it to the tip of one of the highest limbs of my elm. She hung it in scallops between the prongs of a forked twig with light and quick darts.

Returning to the milkweed she tore off another fiber so fine I could not see it, and this she also draped between the twigs in a twirling flight, never alighting to work. All day she wove with spindle neatness until at dusk a misty rope was visible—the handles of her basket. The next day she began to weave the body of the nest by jabbing a thread through the outside, winging up into the inside to receive it and to pull it through. She always flew, her body the shuttle.

The oriole worked almost steadily for twelve days, as compared to the usual four to five days required for a robin to build. As she neared the bottom, she wove only from the inside, turning and twisting until the construction danced as if in a hurricane. When her nest was complete it hung against the spring sky, a credit to the finest weaver.

The long-tailed tailor bird of Asia uses whole leaves, but sensibly sews them together by poking holes, pushing plant fibers through, knotting them and stuffing the cradle with plant stems, wool, and down.

Nesting materials also include feathers, hair, spider webs, snake skins, mud, and the artifacts of man. An electric light bulb was found in an eagle's nest, and paper clips, bottle tops, coins, paper, string, gum wrappers, and buttons have been tucked into the nests of house sparrows.

In size, bird homes vary from less than an inch (the tree swift and hummingbird) to a nest twenty-feet deep and nine feet wide (the Florida bald eagle). This nest is an exception even for an eagle, who as a species makes the second largest nest. The biggest hardly looks like a bird's nest, being built of dirt by Australia's mound builders or megapodes. This is regularly a twelve by twelve foot pile of soil scratched up by the males and occasionally by the females. In it are many chambers of fermenting leaves. When the female is ready to lay, the male opens the mound, waits for the egg to be deposited, covers it, and then turns over the incubation to the warmth of decomposition.

It is a parrot of Africa that has discovered the most obvious way to transport materials to its nesting site, yet it is the only bird that has done so. The parrots of the genus *Agapornis* (there are about five or six species) dwell along the forest edge from the northern savannas of Africa just south of the Sahara to the Orange River. During the nesting season, they snip broad leaves from trees, hold them in their feet, and cut them into long strips. These they tuck into their feathers and "truck" them on wing to their tree hollows where some fashion them into a soft pad for the eggs and young and others weave the cuttings into an elaborate inner chamber with a tunnel leading to the entrance.

Each species cuts the leaves into shapes typical of its breed, some being small and circular, others long and straight. The colorful little birds then tuck them one at a time anywhere on the body except among the flight feathers, which they

*The parrot carrying leaf strips*

leave free for obvious reasons. One species prefers to stuff long strips into the rump feathers, sometimes as many as seven at a time. Bedecked with these cuttings it takes off for its home site looking more like a porcupine than a bird.

The flight of the parakeet is vigorous, and so the holding feathers have special microscopic hooklets that do not grip the bits of nesting materials but rather grip the feathers more firmly to one another to prevent the tucked material from

falling out. In captivity these pretty birds with their colorful
eye rings and brightly marked tails cut paper instead of leaves,
and given the opportunity will sail to their nests sparkling
with ads from magazines, letters, and current bills.

There is no nest, however, like that of the baya bird of
India. It apparently needs not one but two homes. Each is
shaped like a flask with a hole at the bottom. One is con-
siderably larger than the other, and in it are two rooms, an
upper where the mother, eggs, and tiny young abide, and a
lower to which the mother moves the youngsters when their
eyes open. Here they meet and are fed by their father. The
other flask is even more fascinating. It belongs to the male,
and is his domain, a retreat from the family. Astonishingly,
it is decorated with daubs of clay into which—the natives in-
sist—the baya bird pokes lightning bugs.

The Carolina wren holds the record for diversity of nesting sites. Ornithologist Amelia Laskey found that of thirty-
seven birds, seventeen put their nests in bird boxes, nine built
on shelves or ledges of buildings, four among growing plants
in window boxes, two in a sack of old clothes hanging in a
hen coup, and the rest in odd places such as a large paper
sack of seeds, an outdoor cupboard, a crevice between a house
wall and rainspout, a quilt hanging in a garage, a small wall
basket at the front entrance of a house, a newspaper delivery
cylinder, and an open mail box.

At the other extreme are birds like the black skimmer that
build no nest at all, but lay their eggs on the ground, and the
fairy tern uses the bare crotch of a tree. Fortunately these
parents have precocious young who soon break out of the
shell, dry, and feed themselves.

In the darkest burrows and tree hollows are the homes of
the secretive mammals, dwellings that I found singularly dull
compared to bird nests until I discovered that there are many

*Baby otters tied for the night*

specialized mammal dwellings. Some are not unlike human
dwellings, used for different purposes. Interesting are the
rest homes of mammals that vary from the "form" of the
cottontail rabbit, a body fitting depression in a clump of grass
or a brier patch, to a dead banana leaf used as a "motel" by
a tropical opossum of South America during the day. The
latter is strictly for travelers; the same animal rarely returns
to a leaf a second time.

Field mice are not so casual about their rest homes; they
dig permanent holes in the ground of walnut-size and shape
in which they prefer to nap rather than in their elaborate and
seemingly safer tunnels.

In the ocean where the currents carry floating objects in
many directions, families of sea otters rest in kelp beds at
night. At dusk, turning and twisting in the seaweed, a group
of them will bind themselves together in a raft of ropes that
may drift for miles while they sleep, but which keeps them
together until dawn.

Marsh rabbits of the swamps and waterways of the south-
eastern United States (unusual bunnies in that they dive and
swim) cut reeds and pile them into tidy platforms. They sit
safely upon these during the day, and they seem to serve no
other function than for resting.

A tent-like rest home is made by the bats of Panama, *Uroderma bilobatum,* who bite the ridges on the underside of palm leaves to bend them into an A-frame abode. They hang in clusters upon the clipped ridges, sometimes as many as twenty under one leaf, to avoid drenching rainstorms and the penetrating rays of the sun.

Occasionally a mammal will build an elaborate structure just for eating. Our North American muskrat makes a foot-high mound of reeds and sticks in the middle of a pond and ingeniously drills a tunnel into it that leads down to the plant roots these animals feed upon. Useful in summer, these platforms are essential in winter when ice otherwise locks the muskrats away from their food.

Another specialized dwelling is the thermal house or winter nest of the fox squirrel of the mid-Atlantic states. This building reveals an uncanny knowledge of materials and a principle of insulation only recently applied to thermal underwear—dead air spaces. In early autumn this squirrel cuts the tough twigs of oaks and other durable woods with uncanny knowledge and weaves them into a globe high in a tree. Within this frame it places large leaves and presses them against the twigs while damp to form a hard wind- and rain-resistant wall. Then by filling the structure with shredded leaves and the inner bark of trees, the fox squirrel creates dead air spaces that will hold out the cold and hold in the heat of the animal's body. These winter homes are so durable that they last for five to six years without repair.

A few mammals put all these special-use devices into one dwelling to build the most human-like of houses. An elaborate system of burrows and rooms dug deep into the earth is the home of the chipmunk. Not only does this cheerful rodent of North America build a winter room filled with insulating material like the fox squirrel's, but he provides for the days when it is too cold to be abroad: food lies under his bed.

Loving privacy, the chipmunk also builds a nursery and

carpets it with moss and soft rootlets, "pantries" where nuts and seeds are stored (as well as under his own bedding), and yards of tunnels to provide himself with exercise tracks through which he can run during snowy weather. Long before man provided himself with inside plumbing, this clever animal built his latrine, a small room just off his bedroom, dug not only in loose gravelly soil, but below the bedroom, so the effluence would drain into the ground, not back into his den.

Drainage is also understood by the Texas prairie dog who lives where flash floods can be fatal to a ground dweller. To prevent flooding the prairie dog constructs a mound around the entrance of his den, but should water rush in, the engineer is prepared. The burrow is built straight down for as many as six feet, then angles upward to create an airlock that holds the water back until he can dig out.

Of all mammal homes, it is the abode of the North American gray wolves that show the best understanding of the needs of growing young. In the wind-torn wilderness of Mount McKinley National Park, where Olaus Murie studied these magnificent beasts in 1940, the wolves began digging welping dens in late April or May, usually taking over an old fox den and enlarging it. When complete the entrance is about fifteen inches high and twenty inches wide, and the tunnel six to twelve feet long. This opens into the welping chamber in which the young are born April through June. Off the main tunnel are smaller chambers that are used only by the pups and that lead out of the earth to brushy cover or under protective stones where they can see the world without being seen. As they grow, a playground is scooped out before the main entrance of the den by the adults, an area that is enlarged constantly as the little wolves develop.

About fifty yards from the den in the timber or along a wash are three to six beds (depending on the size of the pack), some as deep as eight inches, in which all adults lie and guard the young after they are about a month and half old and no longer sleep with their mother.

In early July when the pups begin to wander off the playground, the adults move them to a summer home. It is less elaborate than the one in which they were born, being only about ten feet long and open at both ends, simply a place to hide from enemies and rest safely when tired. Mr. Murie, one of the outstanding naturalists of this century, found one of these adolescent shelters, and noted later: "The adults were often seen, but the pups were not traveling with them. They were apparently at their rendezvous."

In November the wolves move again, this time to camps on bluffs and promontories where they sleep out in the cold, their homes marked only by slicks of ice where the snow has melted under their warm bodies. At these outposts the gray wolves rest in the continual twilight of winter, high above the abundant life of the tundra. This, finally, is the adult home of the magnificent nomadic hunter of North America.

Of all mammal homes, the most legendary is that of the beaver of North America, and rightly so. From Canada and Alaska south to the marshes of Texas and Louisiana, this once abundant rodent builds one of the wonders of animal engineering—the beaver compound. It is to mankind both a delight and a nuisance.

The project begins when a young beaver couple pairs off in summer, usually for life. They leave the parent lodge and start up streams and creeks searching for suitable territory where aspens and food trees grow in abundance. Once found they will stick to their dam site despite dynamite, creosote, and floods, abandoning it only for one reason—when there is no more food.

The dam, rather than the lodge, is built first. Small sticks are thrust between stones into the bottom mud, butt end upstream. Upon these are laid and wedged larger and larger logs, the gaps filled with selected stuff. Every available material is used, live wood, dead wood, mud, grass, rocks (sometimes weighing forty to sixty pounds), even railroad ties. Crowbars and beaver dam demolition equipment left overnight by railroad men attempting to destroy dams flooding their road beds have turned up in repaired dams the next morning.

Broad at the bottom, narrow at the top, wedged against the upstream side, a beaver dam is shaped almost exactly like Grand Coulee, Hoover, and other man-made constructions. The beaver dam, however, goes up as the water leaks, the animals using the overflow as a level to guide the erection. Sometime before completion spillways are constructed to carry off excess water, useful in time of flood when conduits are opened wide to prevent damage to the dam. When done, these dams range in size from a few feet, to a record four thousand feet in a lake near Berlin, New Hampshire.

Behind a large dam beavers live in colonies, setting up housekeeping with their children if there is sufficient food. All work for the sake of the dam and the colony in the manner known as being "busy as a beaver." Very often a colony will continue to build smaller dams upstream to alleviate pressure on the main dam, a terracing that is comparable to the rice paddies of Asia. Beaver terraces are often invaluable to American farmers in the valleys below, for they serve to stop floods high up in the hills and increase fish and bird populations.

As the food supply at the water's edge is cut and eaten, the dam is built higher to flood a wider and wider plain and bring the beaver to new resources. In summer his food is emergent waterplants and shore grasses; in winter it is strictly the bark of aspens and willows.

After the dam is built, the lodges or homes go up, and these require the most ingenuity, for they must endure the pressure of ice in winter and the activities of the beavers all year. House raising begins by anchoring sticks in the mud, usually in the middle of the pond where they will be safe from predators. On the anchors are thousands of sticks that eventually form a firm dome above the water. Long sticks are trimmed to fit the contour, their clippings added to the pile. When the structure is almost completed, mud is poured into the cracks and crevices. Dug from the bottom of the pond, it is carried between the chin and the chest (not on the tail) and hauled up the lodge to an appropriate dumping spot on top. It seeps down through the sticks, dries, and cements the superstructure together. The top is not sealed but left open like a chimney to provide ventilation for the room below.

The mass erected, the beavers then chew underwater entrances into the lodge where they make above-surface rooms, large enough for their communal way of life. Here they rest and eat in winter and here in the spring the young are born.

Before giving birth the female makes a bed by cutting sticks into long shreds with her incisors and placing them like a mat on the floor of her room. They make an excellent bedding for a mother who comes home wet, for wood shreds drain well and do not rot or decay as grasses do.

One other construction completes the housing project of the beaver, a hole or tunnel that leads underground from the pond to a cover in the woods some forty or fifty feet inland. These are plunge holes into which the animals dive when threatened by their enemies—the coyote, wolf, lynx, bobcat, mountain lion, wolverine, bear, and otter.

Beaver dams do cause trouble as the animals build them higher and higher, lift the water level, and submerge roads, train tracks, streamside buildings, and docks. Despite this the animals elicit nothing but praise even from the men who try to undo their work. In the Colorado Rockies one summer, scientists at the Rocky Mountain Biological Station struggled for weeks to destroy a beaver dam that was flooding the only road to town. They tore the dam down by day, and every night the beavers built it back. This went on until it became a research project, for the dam became not smaller, but bigger and more ingenious as the animals pitted their wits against the demolition squad and came up with new ideas. One morning the mammalogist returned to camp with a grin to report that huge trees had been brought in during the night and laced together so firmly that it took three men three hours instead of one to break the barrier. With that, an RBL official suggested that the beavers be live-trapped and carried off to a distant site, and box traps were set that evening. By dawn the treadles had been sprung by sticks and the boxes were part of the dam.

The only procedures that remained—guns, poisons, and steel traps—were no test of the beaver's endurance, so the scientists preferred to settle the research project by cutting a new road around the edge of the beaver pond.

Although the beaver impoundment is an engineering achievement, the home of the fabulous water ouzel is the most breathtakingly beautiful of all the animals, for this delicate song bird lives in a thundering waterfall. From the Rockies to the Andes from the Alps to the Himalayas in the rarefied air of those mountain tops, in and out of cascades fly the dippers, the Cinclidae. About robin-size and closely related to the wrens, these wonderful birds have adapted to the most beautiful spots in the world, the alpine falls.

When I learned about the water ouzel or dipper, almost fifteen years ago, I set out the next summer for its homeland ten thousand feet up in the Colorado Rockies. The dawn after my arrival I walked through the ghost town of Gothic, an abandoned silver-mining camp whose sun-blackened cabins and hotels contrasted sharply with the bright meadows of alpine flowers, and took the trail to Vera Falls. As I stood before this column of lace that plunges fifty feet into a crystal pool among the Douglas fir and aspens, I saw a small brown

bird fly into the falls. I knew that the bird nested beside waterfalls, but to see one plunge into it startled me so, that I looked
into the pool to see if it had been hurled there. As I did so,
I blinked, for there running along the bottom beneath three
feet of clear water was another bird. It was jabbing at insect
larvae that clung to the bright pebbles. The underwater
walker then pumped its wings and surfaced, and I beheld
a stubby-tailed songbird bobbing around like a duck, its
feathers dry upon emergence, its webless feet somehow propelling it swiftly along. When it took off from the water and
flew into the falls I realized I had found what I had journeyed
across the continent to see, *Cinclus mexicanus*, the water ouzel
of the American Rockies. Stepping up on a boulder I could
see the two birds in back of a thundering wall of glass. They
were preening their feathers on a slender ledge in an air-
pocket behind the cascade. The male dropped, maneuvered
corridors of air, came out of the falls near the bottom, alighted
on the pool, and dove. Once more I beheld a bird hopping
around on the bottom of a stream, and the weary, hot days
crossing the plains and desert seemed a small price to pay for
the opportunity to behold the dipper. The female shot out of
the thundering water and flew up and over the falls where
she alighted on that racing area of no return, the edge of the
cascade. I hastily climbed the cliff, stepping over damp ferns
and wet forests of varicolored mosses. White glacier lilies
sparkled like stars in crannies and niches, and Mayflies danced
in the blue-black shadows the trees cast. If, I thought, I must
choose the home of one of the animals in which to dwell, I will
live with the water ouzel in the magnificent cascades of the
high country.

The remainder of the summer was spent studying the nest
and young of this wondrous bird. The nest was not hard to
find. A round dome of mosses, it was on the wall of the canyon
just above the thundering water where spray kept the mosses
growing and to which no predator could gain entrance.

Beneath it the water churned and splashed as it sped to plunge fifty feet and rush on toward the valley miles below.

A precarious beam placed across the wild flume afforded me infrequent looks into the nest. On that July day there were five eggs. On the following morning there were five babies. Now, I wondered, how did the clumsy babies, when ready to fly, get from the nest, across the sweeping current to the shore? For fourteen days I watched the parents feed the young, roost under the falls, dive, walk, swim, pop around like corks in this incredible environment where no mammal, let alone another bird, had dared to live. On the fifteenth day the answer was obvious. Twelve days in the nest was the longest I had observed in a songbird, but these youngsters obviously were not going to fly until they could soar. On the fifteenth day those skills were gained, and the young stepped from their nests, flapped their wings for hours, then took to the air. They sailed out over the flume, the falls, the beach, and landed gently on the shore.

The other fascination of the dipper is its apparent lack of adaptations for such a world. It does not have webbed feet like a waterbird, it does not have rich oil glands like a duck, and yet it is equally if not more aquatic. While banding one of the parents I had the opportunity to examine closely the tools of a creature of the waterfalls, and the only adaptations I could see were slender and very sharp claws that held them to rocks under water, sleek contour feathers that the water ran off of, and a dense pillow of down between that warded off cold; hardly tools a man would design for the job. Unmeasurable and unseen however, was the most valuable tool of the dipper, the knowledge stored in the cells of the brain that told it how to make use of a current, an eddy, a ripple, and still water.

When the birds are perching on rocks and shores they bob up and down, hence the name dipper, and their white eyelids flash as they speak to each other over the roar of the falls, for although they are some of the most beautiful singers of the bird world, most of their tinkling music is lost in the din of their environment.

Not long ago while I was hung up in a traffic jam in a blue haze of automobile exhaust, I looked west over the Hudson River toward the land of the water ouzel. Somewhere beyond my sight, on a mountain where there were no highways, a water ouzel ran in and out of a crystal stream, sang to his mate, and preened behind curtains of water. As I saw the wondrous bird in my traffic-clouded mind I knew I had been born to the wrong species. Were I a water ouzel, I thought, I would swim through this pool of cars, walk the bottom of the Hudson, and take to the air with a song.

CHAPTER 6

# UNUSUAL PARENTS AND YOUNGSTERS

UNTIL I had children of my own, a parent was a parent and babies were helpless, needed to be loved, fed, and put to sleep. There was, I thought, not much more to it than that.

I began to change my opinion when my daughter was a month old and I was chained to the diaper routine. At this impressionable time, I learned that young songbirds take care of their body wastes in a fecal sac or thin membrane in which the nestling's excrement leaves the body. These appear immediately after the baby bird is fed. It turns its rear end toward the rim of the nest and delivers to its parent a tidy sac that is carried away from the nest site and dropped. Impressed as I was by this, I did not pursue ingenious parents and young until I had three children. That year, at the Institute of Marine Sciences, Miami, a young student working among bubbling tanks of sea life, mentioned a male fish that reared its young. I was ready to listen. When he told me more I knew I had overlooked a rich and varied vein.

"The gaff-topsail catfish," he said, "is a mouthbreeder. It holds its eggs in its mouth during their incubation period." To this day that fish has never lost its position at the top of my list, for he is not only an incredible male, but an incredible parent.

Under the sea waves that roll over the continental shelf

97

*Catfish taking in his young*

from Panama to Cape Cod, this particular catfish wears, in
addition to the whiskers of his group, a triangular dorsal fin
that is tall and sail-like—hence his name gaff-topsail. But in
addition to this distinction, he heeds a remarkable programming from some exotic behavioral computer within him. In
June and July he seeks out a ripe female, and after a brief
courtship induces her to lay. As the huge eggs appear—each is
about three-quarters of an inch in diameter!—he fertilizes
them and takes them into his mouth, sometimes as many as
fifty. This mass he carries night and day for sixty-five days
without relief and without eating. Only about twenty-two
inches long himself, he holds his burden until they hatch.
Even then he does not leave them to fend for themselves but
carries them protectively in his mouth. Swimming into seaweed or sponge beds on the sea bottom, he spits out his young,

and stands guard while they eat. If one becomes dusty with silt which can kill it by clogging its pores, he sucks it into his mouth, rinses it off, and evacuates it with spit shot that jets the fry into the midst of the wriggling cluster of his siblings. When the feeding hours of this nocturnal fish are over, the father collects his large family in his mouth again and settles on the ocean floor, holding them while he and they sleep.

So sensitive is this fish to the identity of his own young that when a striped bass fry was placed among the gaff-topsail catfish babies in a laboratory experiment, the father took it into his mouth along with his fry at bedtime, but when it was time for the family to forage again he did not spit it out!

The devotion of this father to his offspring continues until they are about three inches long, an enormous size for a seemingly average-sized mouth. Fortunately a precise length turns off the parental programming, and the father spits out his young for a last time. Should one turn and come back, the father no longer recognizes it and eats it.

Both parents of the yellow catfish of the fresh-water streams of North America tend their eggs and young. After the eggs are laid in a nest on the silty bottom, they hover over them taking them into their mouths to clean and aerate them, stirring them occasionally with their fins and bony chin barbels to change their positions and keep the developing embryos from sticking to the shell walls. In due time they hatch into tiny black fry, bewhiskered like their parents, and are chaperoned by the adults around the quiet edges of ponds and streams like a cluster of little French schoolgirls. If one strays the mother or father pursues it, takes it into its mouth, and spits it back into the group that moves through the water like a ball. These delightful families can be seen in June and July in their range in eastern United States, for they keep to the shallow edges of waterways and ponds.

Few other fish go so far as the catfish in the care of eggs and young, but the male brook stickleback, a two- to three-inch sparkler of the streams and estuaries of Europe and North America, builds a nest and attends his eggs. The nest is constructed of tiny sticks and weeds that he cements together with mucous cords secreted by his kidneys. This dwelling resembles a spherical bird's nest even to its being lodged on a plant stem or submerged twig, and the male becomes most protective of it. If a neighbor male stickleback or an unripe female approaches his nest, he will drive them off aggressively. Should they linger, he stands on his tail and displays his red belly, a sight that throws the fear of the male stickleback into trespassers and sends them darting away. If, however, a ripe female approaches his home and he threatens her, she signals her condition by standing on her tail and revealing her egg-swollen belly of silver. Seeing this the male swims toward his nest, forgets what he has seen, turns to attack, is shown the belly again, and leads on. The attack and retreat become a zig-zag courtship dance which stimulates the male to show the ripe female his nest and her to peer into the door. As she does so he turns on his side and pushes her in backwards with such violence that, head out the door, she gives forth her eggs.

While she lays, he guards her, swimming around and around the three-quarter inch nest until the last is laid and she has no round belly to show, a sight that evokes aggression in him again. He drives her away. Swirling back to his home, he pours milt on the eggs, then takes up a valiant watch at the door. Fanning his tail for nights and days he wafts fresh water over the eggs to supply them with oxygen and chases away other sticklebacks who come to eat them. As the hatching date arrives, many nervous stickleback fathers can be seen on a warm June day in the edges of purling country brooks fanning frantically in front of their nests or darting at enemies. When the eggs hatch, the father's work is done. He abandons his home, swims to the nest of a neighboring male, and tries to eat his eggs.

*The stickleback: female in the male-built nest*

Attentive parents among the reptiles are rare. Most are like the fish, laying their eggs and departing. A few, however, care for their eggs simply by retaining them in their bodies until hatching time. In North America these are the rattlesnakes, water and garter snakes, water moccasins, and copperheads. They give birth to live young enclosed in a transparent membrane from which some escape immediately, others in hours. The birth is unhurried, a mother snake often resting between arrivals or slipping out to eat. However, when the job is finished, females slide away and leave their young to fend for themselves.

Egg-laying reptiles bury their eggs in sand or soil and give them to the sun-warmed earth to brood. One exception is the American alligator of our southern swamps and bayous. This female not only guards her eggs vigilantly but watches over her young for more than a year by keeping her water hole weeded and providing a balance of life.

A mother alligator's devotion to her young is a moving sight to behold. One August morning in the Everglades National Park, where my father is an ecological consultant, he and I came upon a female alligator digging out the last of her forty-odd hatchlings from a huge mounded nest not far from the road. She was grunting and calling into her nest which was made up of heat-giving vegetation in the process of decay, and where her eggs had been incubating for about sixty-five days. She was answered by high buried grunts. Swiftly she dug toward each sound, her awkward claws as skillful as hands as they freed first one, then another baby 'gator from the incubator.

As they scrambled down the ancient mound (some alligator nests are a thousand years old) the birds and raccoons moved in to feast on the tasty brood. The mother took care of a great blue heron with one swing of her powerful tail and drove off a raccoon with a lunge; then turned and followed her agile babies. As she came to the road she grunted, and they dove under her huge body as she led them across the opening. Slashing her tail, lunging at enemies, bawling, she took them the short distance from the road edge to a reed-rimmed water hole where they plopped and disappeared. The last we saw of the valiant mother, she was streaking toward a chamber-like cave that she and her ancestors had dug under the shore of the pool, and where, my father told me, she would guard her young during the next months when alligator babies are a tempting meal not only for land animals, but also for the snapping turtles and bass of her water home.

The dark caves, or 'gator chambers, are ingeniously arranged so that mother and young can see enemies and act as they move against the light. If a snapper approaches, the babies dart to the shore of the cave, the mother strikes, and the marauder is smashed in her jaws. She crunches it as if it were a cracker, but cannot swallow it neatly for she is tongueless and lipless. However, the falling pieces of prey bring the babies swarming around her like bees at a sugar pot, and the sloppy mother becomes a useful one as she smashes the food.

The turtle may be an enemy of the young 'gators, but he is also, together with the garfish, a main staple in the adult's diet, and so he is not only tolerated, but becomes part of the farm that the 'gator cultivates to the benefit of their young and a host of other animals. The farming process produces a remarkable sequence of events. Water lilies, arrowheads, algae, and seaweed grow rapidly in the sun-warmed alligator holes and can fill a pool solid in a few weeks, forcing the turtles out. But the alligators weed their holes almost daily. With nose and claws they bulldoze the vegetation ashore in an instinctive effort to keep the water open and increase the fish and turtle populations. The debris on shore forms a compost heap in which the seeds of trees and shrubs take root and grow. The plants then shelter the hunting birds and mammals who come to the holes to feed on fish, snails, and crustaceans, and occasionally are harvested themselves by the keeper of the hole. So important is this water farmer to the Florida Everglades that much of the wildlife is dependent upon it, particularly during the dry winter season when the water in the glades disappears and only the deep 'gator holes and a few sloughs remain in the prairies of sawgrass.

Although a rare fish or reptile will tend its young, all birds and mammals provide care for their offspring. The heavily preyed upon defend, not only their own young, but the future of their race. They do this, of course, through fecundity, and no other North American mammal bears and tends as many young as the field mouse, Microtus.

Mammalogist Vernon Bailey found that this short-tailed brown mouse that makes tunnels through the matted grass of meadows and nests in cozy ground holes, produces more young than any other mammal. One female he raised had seventeen consecutive litters within a year and she showed no signs of being at the end of her breeding season. Furthermore as she produced so did her daughters of that season, one of which had thirteen families before she was a year old. If Bailey's original female had had only five babies per litter, a moderate number, she would have produced eighty-five young, and if each of these had had five litters of five, there would have been at least 2125 field mice in Bailey's cage at the end of the year, making this mouse the reproductive assembly line of the mammalian class.

Since few birds or mammals can protect their species by producing such numbers, others have resorted to ingenuity, and the African and Asian hornbills certainly stand close to the top of the list of inventive parents.

The males are enormous, some of them exceeding five feet. Most are between two and five, dark black or brown with bold patches of white or cream on their bodies, wings, and tails. Their beaks look like huge wire clippers and often are sculptured or serrated along the edges. On their heads the hornbills wear a casque or helmet that may be hollow, filled with combs, or solid ivory-like material.

Hornbills live in dense forest or open country and travel in flocks of a dozen or so until the breeding season is upon them. Then the pairs, which are usually mated for life, go off to a cave or a hollow tree to nest. When the female is ready to lay, she steps into the hole and is sealed in by the male of the same species, by both sexes in most cases. The males eat mud, dirt, and their own feces, and coughing it up in pellets mixed with saliva, the odd pair plasters up the hole until only a slit remains in the prison wall that eventually hardens to a cement-like plaster. Through this hole the male passes berries and fruits to the incubating female. When the young hatch, the mother does not come out to help the father, but lets him quadruple his efforts and feed the two or four young as well as herself. During this time the male flys almost continuously,

*Hornbill sealing in its mate*

bringing food supplies to the nest to feed his ravenous family. Not until the nestlings are almost full grown, their wings well developed, their down feathers gone, do the male and female struggle to break the cement and free the children and mother. By this time the male is thin and gaunt. When inclement weather strikes, many hornbill fathers drop dead.

One autumn day a hunter told me that he had seen a female bobwhite quail pick up her young under her wings and run with them to safety. Excited by his observation, I was about to list her in my parent file when a reputable ornithologist told me that it was not true. "No bird," he said, "carries young under its wings." That was ten years ago. Last year at Cornell University's Ornithological Laboratory at Sapsucker Woods I heard the lovely story again, and this time it was verified with pictures. The bird, however, was not a quail, but that remarkable water lily traveler, the jacana of Africa.

John B. D. Hopcraft, ornithologist, had seen and photographed the wondrous baby carrier on a June morning as the sun was rising over Lake Naivasha, Kenya. A female strutted across the lily pads followed by three five-day-old chicks. As Hopcraft rowed toward them the mother gave her alarm cry, the chicks crouched and "froze" motionless. Drifting to within three feet of the downy young, the ornithologist still could not induce them to run, but the frantic parent was fiercely active. She dove at him screaming and crying in distress and finally landed about twenty feet away to feint a broken wing, a bird trick that is used by many species to lure enemies from nests and young. Hopcraft, respecting her anxieties, rowed back several yards, stopped, and watched. Cautiously the mother approached her chicks, periodically halting to eye the ornithologist. Upon reaching them she crouched down, churred softly, and opened her wings. The babies scurried into the shelter and disappeared from Hopcraft's sight. Adjusting herself, the mother gave a single piercing cry, stood up, and, pressing her wings firmly to her sides, walked over the lily pads, chicks under each wing, their long toes dangling out. As she carried them out of danger she stopped once to look at Hopcraft and once to bend down and check her downy burden. She then trotted about fifty feet and put them down.

That more birds do not carry their young under their wings seems surprising, but no species other than the jacana does this habitually. Several individuals, however, have been observed to tote their young in other ways. Recently two enterprising ornithologists, Paul Johnsgard of Nebraska and Janet Kear of the Wildfowl Trust, England, rounded up all the published notes on baby carrying and assembled them in one report. Each incident is breathtakingly beautiful. On a cool day in Greenland, A. Pedersen of Copenhagen saw two barnacle geese fly down from a high cliff with fuzzy objects in their bills. Upon creeping up to them, he saw that the objects were downy young. On another occasion a sheep rancher in Chile observed black-necked swans with their young on their backs flying overhead like a true Mother Goose. In another part of the world a man told of a pair of ruddy shelducks that brought their young to water by tucking them between the neck and shoulder and volplaning from a tall sheer cliff to the shore.

A number of people say they have seen woodducks, those beautiful hole-nesting ducks of the North American woodlands, bring young from high cavities on their backs or in their bills. Expert ornithologists have never seen this, however, for these ducklings get down by themselves, jumping often as many as forty feet to the ground where they skid on their bellies, pick themselves up, and run like wound-up toys behind their mothers to the water.

I raised one of these charming hatchlings in a bathtub for a few days and was amused to watch its behavior the first hours of its life. It leaped almost constantly two and three feet into the air in an effort to gain the side of the tub, a position it instinctively sensed would be the doorway to the woods. This lasted about a day; then the jumping clock ran down and the duckling paddled around the tub pecking at food on the bottom. Since these birds are difficult to raise, I released it on the fifth day inadvertently facing it toward the lane. Without being able to see the water, it turned around and ran up through the woods toward the pond with an in-born knowledge of the earth that seemed miraculous in one so small and unschooled.

The birds widely known for carrying their young on their backs are, of course, the glorious, mute, black-necked and black swans. Even among these species, however, the trait is not universal but regional, for the carriers live only in the temperate zones, the same swans in colder Arctic regions brooding their young instead of carrying them, a behavior that leads ornithologists to believe that back riding in the warmer climates is a substitute for brooding. Whatever it is, it is initiated by the cygnets who approach a male or female and climb aboard between the folded wing and the tail. The parent does not assist beyond remaining motionless until the crew is settled in, a sight that evokes in the human observer the deepest feelings of joy and security.

Wild parents are not always so personally attentive to their young. A few provide for their children's care by turning them over to others, a system that is used by some people and about seventy-eight species of birds. These lay their eggs in the nests of others and leave them for foster parents to in-cubate in a process known in the bird world as "parasitism."

A half-hearted parasite is the black duck of North America who will lay in another nest more out of ignorance or love of a nest than any deliberate planning on her part, and this may be how such behavior once started. At the bottom of my hill in Poughkeepsie, New York, was such a black duck. One May morning a female was walking back to her nest by a circuitous route when she came upon the nest of a white farm duck, eyed it, and then settled down and laid an egg. On the following morning she returned to her nest via the stream and laid in her own nest, eventually winding up with five of her own. The farm duck on the other hand, had twenty-two in her nest—many of them laid by the black duck—and was hard pressed to spread herself from one side of this mass to the other.

The South American black-headed duck who lives in the marshlands of Argentina and Chile, does not build a nest at all, nor does she lay eggs in other ducks' nests, but in those of the ibis, herons, spoonbills, and about ten other waterfowl. Mannerly little birds, the hatchlings never impinge on their hostess but, cracking out of their shells before their step-siblings, make use of the warm mother to dry, then wiggle out from her feathers without disturbing her for more than a startled instant. They climb down to the water and take up a solitary and secretive life in the tall rushes. Each lives alone never approaching one of its own species until toward the end of summer when some inner signal tells one black-headed duck what another black-headed duck is, and they gather in quacking flocks.

In North America it is the brown-headed cowbird that is truly and wholeheartedly parasitic. Not only does it never build a nest, but it leaves its egg and chick to the complete care of its host, whose own offspring are almost always eliminated by the aggressive parasite. The baby cowbird hatches before the others and often has a day's start on its foster siblings when they step out of their eggs. By this time it can reach higher and scream louder than the others and gets most of the food. The weaker babies are either trampled to death by the vigorous cowbird or die of starvation. It is rare that any bird parasitized by the cowbird raises anything but a cowbird. In the June and July woods and fields tiny buntings, vireos, and song sparrows are feeding enormous cowbirds often twice their size.

Bird parasitism is a flourishing practice in the Old World

where 47 out of 126 species of cuckoo indulge in this art, and the common cuckoo of Europe is so skilled that it parasitizes three hundred different species. Only one of our cuckoos is parasitic, the others raising their young, which are odd in their own way. The young of the yellow-billed cuckoo has a black leathery skin for weeks. Its feathers grow encased in black pointed sheaths that make the babies appear more like tiny porcupines than birds. These weird looking youngsters can climb rather awkwardly, which they certainly need to do, for their homes of sticks often fall apart soon after they hatch. On fledgling day, however, within a few minutes, a minor miracle happens. The sheaths break open, the young burst into bloom and fly off in a plumage that closely resembles their parents'.

At the opposite pole from the cowbirds and cuckoos are the herring gull parents, whose behavior is so intricately intertwined with the behavior of their young that the two work together in a sort of push-button relationship that almost seems mechanical.

Upon hatching the young herring gulls must be continuously brooded until their plumage is dry. If the parent is disturbed during these critical hours and the young are exposed to the air too long, the downy feathers do not fluff, but stick together and kill the chick.

If all goes well, the chicks dry correctly, then crawl about under the parent, who shifts about and finally gets the message and stands up. With this a miraculous exchange of signals goes off. The chick looks up, sees the red spot on the underside of the parent's bill and is instantly stimulated to strike this with sharp well-aimed blows. The blows set off a reaction in the parent, which stretches its neck. A huge swelling appears, and in moments the old bird has regurgitated an enormous lump of food. Seeing the food and the chick, the next signal goes off and the parent leans down, picks up small offerings, and feeds the youngster.

This behavior of the chicks to strike the red target that starts the feeding is inherited or instinctive, according to Oxford's Niko Tinbergen, who spent almost twenty years studying the herring gulls of Europe. In all his observations he never saw a parent teach a chick to strike. They simply stepped from the egg, dried, looked up, and hit.

Equally fascinating is the fact that the process seems to work both ways. The chick apparently cannot eat without seeing the spot and striking. Several years ago I tried to raise a young herring gull and was about to return the downy two-day-old to the gullery because, although I could force feed him, the food was no sooner down than it was up again. Before leaving I recalled Tinbergen's research and wondered if perhaps the chick needed to hit his target in order to eat. Quickly I painted a red mark on my thumb with a lipstick and held it above the little fellow's head. He struck with a powerful blow and opened his mouth; I stuffed him with half-cooked fish that he swallowed and kept down. After being fed the lipstick method for a few days, he either outgrew this behavior or adjusted to the idea that I was his mother, for he ate without seeing the spot. However, he never got over his love for the color red. Free to wander in and out of the back door and mingle with my family, he struck red shoes, painted

*The feeding-target of the herring gull*

toenails, designs on dresses, mosquito bites, and went so far as to strike the red ink off a book on the bottom shelf of my library entitled *The Herring Gull's World,* by Niko Tinbergen.

The interpersonal relations in a herring gull family grow with the passing of time. Within a few days parents learn to recognize their own chicks, an astonishing achievement in a gullery where there are hundreds and hundreds of downy young as indistinguishable from one another as steel marbles in a bowl. Yet, if a strange chick comes onto the property of a pair of adult herring gulls, he will be attacked and killed. Because of this the young are so cautious about stepping out of their yards that the first few days of my young sea gull's stay in our house I managed to restrain him to newspaper by threatening him. He remained on the paper, until he learned that I could not follow through with my threats, and with that he took off and I moved him to the yard outside.

A strong force that ties the parent herring gull to its young is its appearance. Small, head large for its body, eyes wide (innocent we call it), movements awkward, it can arouse the same parental feelings that we have when we look at a baby, a kitten, or a fawn. To maintain this attitude of tenderness in the parent gulls as long as possible, the herring gull chicks pull in their necks and hunch low to appear smaller than they are. Sometimes they cry and employ all possible ruses to get through the difficult young-adult period when parents are growing intolerant of them.

So universal is the response of adult birds to the awkward movements and cries of the young that among songbirds, adults will feed babies of another species. Robert Graber, a University of Michigan graduate student, put a young incubator-hatched cardinal in the nest of a Bell's vireo after removing the vireo eggs. The naked nestling lifted its head, opened its mouth, and gave the baby "food" cry. Within one minute the adults changed their behavior from that which involves incubation to tending and feeding young. On another occasion Graber removed eggs from a painted bunting nest and replaced them with one bunting and one cardinal hatchling. Again development and species mattered not at all. The adult buntings reacted to the cries of the young, fed them, brooded them, and raised the mixed pair.

Mammals also have their share of exceptional families, and the nine-banded armadillo from Kansas south to Argentina are among the strangest of this class. From one internal armadillo egg that splits and splits come as many as twelve identical twins, but usually four. They are all the same sex and all exactly alike from the number and arrangement of the plates and scales in the armor to the number of hairs in a given area! Born with their eyes open and a soft carapace that hardens gradually with age, the extraordinary youngsters walk when a few hours old and accompany their mother in search of food shortly after birth. When frightened, they roll into identical balls or flatten in identical patterns against the ground, and

*Armadillo, with identical young*

they all trot with a shuffling gait, occasionally getting up on their haunches to travel on two feet. Both adults and young have poor body temperature control, so the burrow of the armadillo is often shared with rabbits and cotton rats.

The family has another unusual habit—the way it swims. At the edge of a pebbly river, mother and identical twins halt a moment to swallow air. They gulp until their stomachs are full, then slide into the water to float like balloons to the other shore. The armadillo young leave home when they are about six months old, some of them pairing up to depart, but most just trotting off alone, perhaps to seek their own identity. Certainly they have found new territory most successfully in recent years. They are now a pest in the Everglades National Park where they are competing with indigenous animals.

Totally unlike the self-sufficient armadillo young, which see when born and walk soon after, are the pampered babies of the marsupials and the gray kangaroo in particular. The young of the order Marsupialia, second from the bottom of the mammalian ladder, weigh less than half an ounce after twenty-nine to thirty-eight days when they leave the uterus. In the animal kingdom this is a long time for these results, the house cat completing its well-furred young in only approximately twenty more days. The speck of kangaroo life is guided by the mother from the vaginal opening with her tongue across her belly to the pocket where it remains almost a year, or 312 days before it is "reborn" and comes out of the incubator to try its feet. After leaving the pouch, the young gray kangaroo is usually suckled for at least another six months! The majority of the world's approximately ninety species of marsupials dwell in Australia, New Guinea, and Tasmania. Marsupials look like rats, mice, cats, wolves, badgers, bears (koala), a fact that makes one wonder just how strong are the influences of the grasses, trees, and forests on the shape of creatures. One family, the opossums, lives in the

Americas. Of the twelve species one dwells in North America, our pointed-nosed ratty-tailed Virginia possum.

When mammals are threatened, their dens discovered, or food becomes scarce in an area, most mothers will carry their young to new sites, and each method of toting is distinctive. Squirrels grab the bellies of their babies with teeth and lips. The young then cooperate by curling their head on one side of the mother's head and their tail on the other to get a purchase that lessens her burden and at the same time gives her a clear view of the road ahead. Cats grip the back of the neck and dogs take the scruffs, but the grizzly and black bears take the entire head of a cub in their mouths to carry them.

Unable to pick up their babies in their mouth, mice use another method. When a mother flees from her nest the babies hold on to her teats as she runs, a system that is not very efficient, for many drop off along the way and are lost in the scramble. However, the infants of the pine mouse are caught in no such predicament; they clutch their mother's teats so hard that they can swing to the right and left, flip up into the air and down, and still not lose their hold.

Offspring of the common shrew of Europe have devised yet another system. When this family is threatened by hawks, foxes, dogs, or man, one baby grabs the tail of its mother in its teeth, another grabs the first baby's tail, and another the next tail, and so on, until they can escape to the woods linked together as one.

Mammary glands are of course unique in mammals and together with hair distinguish them from all other classes. Because of the position of these glands on the warm chests and bellies, and because the infant needs the mother and the mother the infant, the most intimate relationship of all life is between the mammalian mother and child. To nurse by sucking seems so reasonable that I was not aware until recently that there are other mammalian ways of doing this than our

*Family chain of the shrew*

own. But there are. The female spiny anteater, or echidna (not to be confused with the incestivore), a member of the primitive order of Monotremata (egg layers with bird-like skull), who incidentally incubates her egg in a pouch rather than a nest like the platypus, nurses her babies by forcibly ejecting milk into their mouths with a squeeze of the muscles. The babies need only to nudge the glands to turn on this flow of milk. A system somewhat similar to this is used by porpoises and other sea mammals. However, in addition to a jet stream the sea mother has a pocket around each nipple into which her baby can stick its nose while nursing under water. As for the duckbilled platypus (who has no teats to either nurse or squirt), the young feed by licking the milk from hairs down which the fluid drips.

Since this intimacy between mother and young exists in the mammalian world, there was bound to be one beast in which the affection for the young is so great that the feeling of warmth transcends ire and aggression and permeates an entire group. Such a mammal is the African lion, a creature so affected by the presence of babies that the behavior of every member of the pride is changed when the young arrive.

Rudolf Schenkel of the Department of Zoology, University of Switzerland, recently completed a study of the home life of a pride of free-ranging lions in Nairobi National Park, Kenya. His observations, which extended from December 1962 to April 1965 in that golden land of grass, tree islands, and sun, revealed that all the adults love when there are cubs. The pride consisted in the beginning of his study of two adult males, a very old female without cubs, and two females who gave birth to three cubs each in the dense thickets. The mothers were not seen until about the third day after welping when they came back to the pride to visit briefly. Among the adults tensions existed that were expressed in growls and fights.

When the babies were about ten weeks old, peace descended on the pride as the lionesses brought their wide-eyed, wobbly cubs out of the forest and introduced them to their elders in one of the most beautiful ceremonies in the animal kingdom. "The event," writes Schenkel, "has a marked consequence on the pride as a whole. Fighting and squabbling end abruptly, and after the introduction there is practically no room for social conflict and tension for the presence of cubs changes attitudes."

Social relations were impregnated with fondness and tenderness after the introduction. Even the two young lionesses showed as much devotion for each other's cubs as they showed to their own. The males nudged and pawed the youngsters and were gentle with each other. Only the old lioness was occasionally intolerant of the cubs, but even she was pleasant about her feelings. She turned away from the caresses of the cubs with a soft growl.

This peacefulness persisted through the training period. In the early morning the cubs and their mothers would go off together on excursions to the bush and rocky river beds, often joined by the males or the old lioness, who would watch the cubs with relaxed fondness as they investigated the flowing water and listened to the voices of the forest.

When the mothers brought them to their first communal kill, the cubs were not only tolerated by the older lions but taught how to tackle food. Settling down by a cub, a mother or male lion would lick, bite, pull, and gnaw at the meat and induce the young one to join the festivities with friendly growls.

Hunting exercises for the cubs were quiet and playful as the mothers led them to wildebeestes which they chased clumsily and sporadically until they could match action for action in the chase. When the cubs were about five months old, stalking lessons began. A lioness would lie in wait in the grasses until a wildebeeste passed, then she would arise and stalk for about fifteen yards. The cubs would join her, crouching low, their eyes on the prey. When they were completely involved, the lioness would drop out of the sport, generously leaving the cubs to go on until the wildebeeste saw them and ran off. Another type of hunting lesson was given in the evening when the warthogs were active. The mothers would stalk these by using hills and collapsed hyena dens for cover, and the cubs would follow until the warthogs fled. None of these lessons ever ended in a kill, which led Schenkel to believe that they were purely exercises and play.

As hunting lessons progressed, the mood of the pride began to change infinitesimally. A year of growing passed, the females mated again in January and for a few weeks they hunted for their eighteen-month-olds, but as pregnancy advanced they became less and less attached to them and finally ignored them entirely by late February.

Similarly the old lioness and the adult males began to show intolerance toward the adolescents and one another. Intimacy decreased, tensions appeared again, and in April the young animals were no longer tolerated at all. In turn they did not get along with the older members of the pride. Fights ensued, and one day the cubs attacked the old lioness, knocked her over, and threatened her until she crouched low and showed no aggression.

Before the birth of the next litter the juveniles went through a difficult time. They had to kill their own food which

*Fighting young of the whooping crane*

was often robbed from them by the older lions. They fought their elders and each other, and just as the pride seemed to be torn apart—the new kittens were introduced. Peace descended on the pride—all tensions vanished, and once more tenderness prevailed even between the two-year-olds and their elders.

Just as there are lovable babies, so are there diabolical ones, the children of the magnificent vanishing whooping cranes being among the brats of the earth. Two to a nest, the cranelings break out of their egg shells in the lonely bog country of Woods Buffalo National Park, Saskatchewan, dry off, and immediately begin to jab each other with their lance-like beaks. Bodies and eyes are speared, cries go up, and the parents rush between them.

A successful whooping crane family is separate but equal as a mother and one youngster wander the lonely acres in one direction, and the father and the other hatchling hunt the bogs in another. At least a mile of land is needed to raise and keep apart these, the nastiest siblings in the animal kingdom.

# CHAPTER 7

# DINERS OF UNLIMITED IMAGINATION

ABOUT five years ago I accepted an invitation to the annual banquet of the New York Zoological Society. It was to be held in the Grand Ballroom of the Waldorf-Astoria, and I am one who likes the pomp and circumstance that surrounds man's formal eating habits. On the snowy night I arrived early, eased my way through bedecked guests, and took my seat beside an elderly zoologist. We were the only ones as yet at the table, so I commented on the impressive stage setting for the feast, the variety of glasses, silverware, and china. I was promptly told the entire procedure was highly unoriginal and mundane.

"Living with us on this earth," the professor said in Oxford English, "are diners that would make this banquet look bizarre and clumsy. Imagine being so refined you need never open your mouth to eat. There is such an animal. Or try to think of employing chemistry and physics to eliminate the awkwardness of hauling food.

"Then," his eyes twinkled playfully, "silverware of threads or beautifully executed dances instead of these shovels." He picked up a spoon and a fork. "You really must become acquainted with the other diners that share this planet with us before you limit yourself to the admiration of man's table."

Other guests arrived, conversations crackled around us, and I had no opportunity either to learn the professor's name or, more important, to ask him what animal eats without a mouth.

Intrigued by the professor's sophisticated diners, I began to search for them by questioning my scientific friends and acquaintances, and, of course, the mouthless wonder came first. What kind of a face would it have? How would I recognize it? A marine biologist at the Institute of Science, Miami, identified this incredible creature for me. It is the Convoluta, a worm that seems to have imagination and know-how far beyond man's. The little animal feeds upon a farm it grows inside itself.

When the tide goes out in the English Channel, the sands of North Brittany and the Channel Islands of Jersey and Guernsey flash green as colonies of these quarter-inch worms crawl from shallow subterranean hideouts where they have anchored themselves during high tide and stretch themselves to bathe in light and eat without eating, dine without swallowing.

The Convoluta manages this in the course of its life span. In spring when it hatches from an egg, it does at first have a mouth and forages for a certain algae in the sea water and gorges upon it. Soon the Convoluta is green from head to tail, then it eats no more but feeds upon the starches the algae plants manufacture through photosynthesis. Instinctively sensing that sunlight is essential to its garden, the Convoluta spends every moment when the tide is out basking in the light that filters through its transparent body. The light acts on the algae inside so that they can convert the hydrogen, oxygen, and carbon into sugar, then the starches. These the Convoluta absorbs, and so it need eat no more. The oval mouth in its pointed head degenerates from lack of use, its digestive system becomes functionless and almost disappears. Within a few days it cannot eat even if it wanted to, and sunbathing is substituted for foraging as the emerald worms gather in colonies along the beaches, creeping in and out of the summer light to tend their gardens.

Eventually a Convoluta needs more nutrients than starch, and it begins to eat the goose that lays the golden egg. Slowly it devours the algae from its rear end forward until it eats the last morsel and dies of starvation. The sands lose their green color, autumn comes, and a new generation of Convoluta eggs laid in July await the light of another spring.

The Convoluta shelter the algae and cannot live without them. Those raised experimentally in the absence of the plant failed to develop and died.

What an animal eats and how it chews is reflected in the contours of its face. For eating vegetation the rabbit nibbles, then gnaws, then with a rotating movement grinds its food. Consequently its front teeth are mounted in the fore part of a V-shaped jaw bone that affords the leverage of wire cutters. The premolars and molars are well back in the mouth for grinding. Together the muscles and bones that work these teeth give the rabbit that cheeky look and characteristic deep chin. How and what we eat shape our faces, too. Human teeth are designed to chew an omnivorous diet of meat and vegetables. Since we do not have to snip, and because we put our food in our mouths with our hands, we don't have that wire-cutter look of a rabbit. Instead the human face reflects the grinding action of the rabbit plus the slicing or tearing movement of the carnivore. To cut meat, as carnivores do, a muscle near the ear slams the lower jaw down. To mash the vegetables, the muscle that covers our jaw rotates the molars. This, together with the fact that we have not developed the long nose that accompanies a good sense of smell, gives us the flat multipurpose eating face.

The mammals whose faces have been most obviously shaped by their food are the anteaters, which appear in several orders of animals. Sloths, armadillos, aardvarks, Chinese pangolins, and the common anteaters, all of the order Edentata, have long pointed mouths into which fit sticky tongues that are unmistakably designed to hunt in ant hills. Even more perfectly shaped for ant hunting is the mouth of the spiny ant-eater of Australia (an egg layer). This two-foot long termite hunter has a flat hypodermic needle with a hole in the end of it for a mouth. Out of this shoots a seven-inch tongue that so carefully selects only the soft ants that this little fellow has no teeth at all. It is the only mammal that does not have even the vestige of a tooth somewhere in its development.

The bills of birds have specialized most dramatically into instruments designed by and for their food. The black skimmer of the coastal shores of the Americas has a fish lure that it shoves just under the surface of the water to attract fish to the surface. Immediately returning over the same course, it picks them up with a sudden stab. The lower mandible of its bill is longer than the upper and bright orange in color, probably to catch the attention of the fish.

To open spruce and fir cones, the red- and white-winged crossbills of our northern boreal forests have evolved a beak unlike any opener that man has invented. The lower and upper cross each other near the tip and seem to us to be deformed. When shoved between cone scales, the crossed pliers easily pry them apart, and the tongue shoots in and picks up the seed.

The beak of the roseate spoonbill of Florida looks awkward until its purpose is understood. A long beak with a flat spoon at the tip, the bill is swung back and forth in the mud. Into the bill swirls bottom debris that is tested against numerous nerves in the wide spoon, and the living organisms are swallowed, the inert matter washed out.

The need to separate snail-like cerithium mollusks from mud has shaped the odd bill of the rose-colored American flamingo. The beak, looking like the bent bowls of two facing spoons, is shoved along the bottom, the bird's head completely submerged. The tongue pumps in water and a filter separates the food; water is shot up and out the corners of the beak, and the animal food is sent to the stomach where it is ground up by powerful stomach muscles.

The drill of woodpeckers, the hooked-meat ripper of the hawks and owls, the seed crackers of the finches, and the forceps of the flycatchers all tell an ornithologist that a bird eats without examining his menu.

From time to time I kept an eye out for the chemists and physicists that the unknown professor at the Waldorf had mentioned to me. It never occurred to me that he might be inventing animals to tease me, and I suspected that I would find these among the insects for their diabolically clever mouth parts, like the teeth and jaws of the mammals, are a clue to their eating habits. Insects are divided into two groups on the basis of these structures, the chewing insects like the grasshoppers, and the sucking insects like the bedbugs and mosquitoes. The variations on these two themes are seemingly infinite. The highly predaceous dragonfly larva, for instance, has made a trap door of its mouth that it can slam shut on its prey. The sipping butterfly has coiled its mouth into a drinking tube. The gnawing larva of *Fenusa ulmi*, the leaf miner, has developed jagged hooks to saw its way into a leaf.

One glance at the mouth and the head of the giant water bug's family, Belostomatidae, leaves no doubt that this creature is one of the earth's more terrifying eaters. This family of North and South America are chemists of monstrous ability. They hold prey with their forelimbs and pierce the flesh of insect, fish, or frog with their proboscis to inject them with chemicals after ten to fifteen minutes. This brew turns bone, muscle, viscera—everything *except* the skin—into a watery fluid that is drunk through their tubes or proboscises.

These diabolical creatures are fat bugs that are somewhat oval in shape and can be identified readily by their habit of hanging head down on the surface of the water as they watch

*The diabolical water bug*

for prey. The adults, tails up, give comic relief to the dream-like quality of a pond on a summer day, but they fill me with horror. Not long ago as I was pushing my canoe into a lake near my home, I noticed a frog that did not leap with the others at the fall of my foot, and I picked it up. At first it seemed alive, for its eyes were clear and bright, its skin tight and moist. As I turned it over, an insect's mandibles flashed, and a water bug released its hold and dropped into the water. I looked from it back to the frog, which had burst and was draining like a water-filled balloon. Slowly the frog's eyes misted, its toes collapsed, and I held in my hand a limp, form-less skin. I shuddered in witnessing that big frog's body rendered into water by an insignificant insect.

The rapid liquefaction of the tissues is done by a potent mixture of hydrolytic enzyme in the salivary glands, a horrible venom that no man can produce as yet and hopefully never will be able to.

Almost equally talented in grim horror is the aphid lion, a larva that eventually becomes one of the most beautiful of adult insects, a species of the lacewing family. This small creature pierces aphids with its hypodermic-shaped mouth, and slowly sucks out its juices until only the husk remains. Not satisfied with this, the aphid lion then picks up the mummy and hangs it on one of many hooks that protrude from its body. The more it eats and decorates itself, the more successful it becomes as a hunter. Each trophy increases the aphid lion's resemblance to a cluster of living aphids, and the creeping catacomb can then move more and more freely among its prey.

The antlion, the grotesque insect larva of yet another species of the lacewing family, is the physicist that the British zoologist at the Waldorf had referred to. Anyone who has tried to climb a sand pile or dig holes at the beach can understand the principle of the antlion's dining room. Just how this insect discovered the way to grade his sand pile so that one shifted grain will start an avalanche is one of the mysteries of life and death in this world. The larva selects a spot in the dry soil or sand near an ant colony and, kicking in all directions with pin-wheel–like appendages, digs down into the ground creating a cone-shaped depression. Just before the whole thing collapses on the digger, it stops working and leaves its ice-tong shaped claws protruding from the bottom of the pit. In this position it waits for hours or even days on the chance that eventually an ant will walk its way, trip one of the keystone grains of sand at the rim, and ride down to the waiting jaws on the landslide.

On rare occasions the antlion is not quick enough to catch the fallen ant, and the angulation of the pit destroyed, the prey starts to climb out. If the antlion is hungry, the ant never makes it. Before the prey reaches level ground, the larva digs again, pitching the wall of the cone so that with every step forward the ant takes three backward and, as if on a rug, is pulled down to the waiting jaws.

Another physicist also builds a pitfall, the larva of the tiger

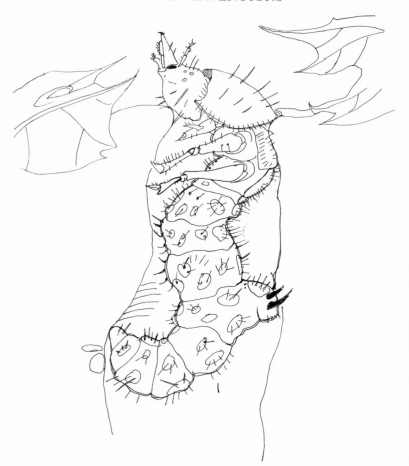

*Doodlebug in its trap*

beetle. Called a "doodlebug," the animal looks like a cross between a disjointed rhinoceros and a worm. Its trap resembles the holes elephant hunters dig and cover with leaves and branches. A skilled workman, this larva digs a vertical pit in the soil often two feet deep. Since it cannot cover the trap with material light enough for an insect to crash through, it

uses its head to plug the hole. Bending its neck at right angles
to its body, its grubby face peers up from the forest floor like
a bit of dirt. The larva holds itself at the top of the pit with
hooks that shoot out from a stout projection on its rump.
Eventually a victim comes along, steps on the doodlebug's
face and is seized. Prey in its jaws, the larva drops into the
shaft. Should the victim be strong and fight back, the larva
employs another mechanical principle to prevent itself from
being hauled from its pit. With a ripple it releases its hooks,
lowers them in the shaft, digs them in again, and pulls downward. With this winch-like action it drags the prey to the
bottom of the shaft, paralyzes and devours it. The doodlebug's
underground table does indeed make the Waldorf seem
mundane.

On occasion, when tired, I have wished that the ceiling
would open and broiled steak drop down. On the other hand,
I have not desired all the animal culinary arrangements I
have discovered, the cutlery of that same liquifying water bug,
the electric-light bug being one. Although I stand in awe of
it, it is a little too humorless, for this bug has a pair of switch-
blades more lethal than carving knives. These tools are
directed to their objective by the two thousand predacious
eyes of this great water bug of North America. The switch
blades, however, are beautifully designed for the purpose of
snagging small fish, tadpoles, and insects. The lower joint of
the front leg fits snugly into a groove in the upper joint and
when closed is not detectable. If a fish passes within range,
the blade flashes open and slams closed. The prey captured,
the large flat-bodied bug then injects it with its powerful
juices.

Although the two-inch long North American species of this
bug is formidable in one way, it is pathetic in another. Swift
swimmers, nasty hunters, they cannot resist an electric light
(hence the name). On a summer night hundreds and thousands will see the sparkle of some distant street light, arise

from the water's edge, and, their switch blades closed, stream toward the light. Circling closer and closer they fly until burned or exhausted. In the morning, piles of brown bodies, their filament wings twisted and broken, cover the ground like fallen leaves.

To fastidious man, a truly appalling eater is the starfish. After it has succeeded in prying open a clam with its hydraulic feet, this animal then throws its stomach out through its mouth (a tiny hole in the center of the star) and slides it into the mollusk through a space, in some cases, as small as one tenth of a millimeter. Once the stomach has entered, some species relax their hold and permit the clam to close upon their own stomach. Amazingly, there is no evidence of any damage. The gap usually increases as the stomach digests the food, but even this is not necessary. A starfish of the California coast, *Pisaster,* according to zoologist H. M. Feder, ate mussels that were bound together with wire to prevent them from separating in an experiment he ran on these incredible diners of the sea.

While on the subject of appalling eaters, something to match it can be said about peculiar diets. The food of animal kind includes, as one might suspect, everything organic—the living, the dying, the dead, and the rotten of both plants and animals. Only one menu, however, truly stands out. The young of the stickflea *Echidnophaga gallinacea* eat the feces of their parents, a diet no other beast has dared to try, as far as I know.

Of all the diners of the animal kingdom, the bola spider, the creature that dines with a thread, is the most sporting. Its prey seems to have a far better chance of living than dying, for this little arachnid of the trees snags flying food in the dark of the night with a single line. It then dines on a table of thread. How it survives is a miracle, for its technique is as if a child dropped a line from the Empire State Building in the hopes of catching a bird. The bola is also quite con-

*The bola spider "fishing" from its swing*

spicuous, a dangerous trait among enemies. Its back is grotesquely adorned with crests and horns, its belly is wrinkled and surrounded with humps. Entomologist Willis J. Gertsch can find no function for the distortions. They are neither deceptions that attract prey or mates nor deceits that fool enemies. The bola is simply a conspicuous creature with a chancy manner of hunting.

The female bola is the wonder. She is the great hunter, as the male consumes only plant juices. By day she hides under leaves near the tips of twigs. When night falls, she runs down her twig to its branch. When she is over an opening in the leaves, she fastens a thread to the underside of the limb and, picking it up so it won't stick to the bark, makes a loose loop and secures it near the tip of her twig. Letting herself down to the middle of this crystal trapeze, she reels out another thread that is several inches long. Down this she pours a load of viscid silk that rolls to the end and forms a sticky ball. She then lets out the line and ball and tests it for balance and weight in order to swing it easily to and fro in any direction. Then she cuts the thread and is ready to fish the night through.

Leaning from her swing and holding the line in her feet, she waits with uncanny patience for an insect to flutter by. Hours, even whole nights pass without success, but she knows the laws of chance, and eventually a moth flutters within the circle of her weapon. Judging the distance to the flyer as well as the speed that it is traveling, the bola swings her line and ball in the direction of the flight, strikes the moth on the underside of its forewing, and waits. The line stretches with the momentum of the flying body and then contracts, bringing the struggling moth back. The spider descends her line, kills her prey with a bite, and swathes it in a sheet of silk; she then carries it up the silver thread to dine on her trapeze among the leaves. Meal completed, the bola drops the empty bundle to the ground, reels in her swing, and goes home for the day. When I first learned of the bola, I remembered the distinguished zoologist who was bored by dinner at the Waldorf, and then I knew why. Humans hardly seem to be in the same league with this epicure of the arachnids.

Another unusual hunter is the archer fish of the fresh-water pools of the South Pacific islands, a pumpkin-seed–shaped animal that is the William Tell of the fish world. Cruising just beneath the surface, eyes peering through water into air, a difficult task in itself, the archer has arrived at the delightful skill of using water as a weapon. When the fish sees a dragon-fly resting on a leaf, he sucks in a volume of water, surfaces, aims, squirts, and knocks the insect from its perch. He snaps and eats, then cruises along again, waiting to use his arrow.

A few of the earth's creatures eat with implements. How they evolved such wondrous behavior is a source of scientific speculation, but this much is known: smart individuals do make discoveries and teach them to neighbors and young. Over the eons this knowledge is stored in the genes to become, if not instinctive, certainly readily learnable within a species. The shrikes of the Old World and the Americas, which are songbirds with hawklike behavior and hook-tipped bills, use tools of a sort. Birds of dashing looks, usually with black eye bands, they do not have the powerful feet and talons of falcons and accipiters but small feet like a robin's. Consequently when they chase a bird or insect, these birds can neither kill with their feet nor hold on to their food while they tear it apart. They deal a death blow with their beaks and bring their prey to the natural skewers of the wild thorns of trees and bushes. Here they impale their victims, not to ensure death, but to secure them while they dine.

The Northern shrike hunts from the top of a tree, scanning the countryside for every moving object, bird, mouse, or insect. When a flock of sparrows passes below, he dives into their midst, gliding between bold wing strokes. As a sparrow twists and dives, the shrike twists and dives, matching every movement of the prey until he drives it to the ground, where he can strike it a mortal blow on the head with his beak.

Now the thorns of the area become the bird's focal point, and he seems to know, like a wolf knows his range, every suitable thorn in his square mile of territory. Taking off from the ground, food in his beak, the hunter flies to a tree, stands above a thorn, and spears his meal. With dainty bites he eats, or if not hungry simply leaves it there until he needs it. Occasionally there are no thorns available, and the shrike either hangs his food on a nail in a post or barn or drapes it by its head from a narrow crotch of a tree like a duck in a Chinese market. The loggerhead shrike, the smaller of two species that range from Alaska through Canada to Mexico and occasionally into the Western states, feeds largely on insects. He hunts from low fence posts and bushes and makes his presence known by impaling locusts and grasshoppers on the barbs of wire fences. I have seen many fences in summer that resemble an entomologist's collection box, telling me that the loggerhead is about.

An even more marvelous tool user is one of the Darwin's finches. This woodpecker finch is a small bird of Barrington Island in the Galapagos, that volcanic cluster of isles that lies 650 miles west of Ecuador. Here dwell some of the most remarkable beasts of the world: the cormorant that cannot fly, the four-foot-long iguanas, and the great lumbering Galapagos turtles. Aboard the *Beagle* Darwin discovered the odd creatures here and was particularly enchanted with the finches, later named after him.

Of them all, however, the woodpecker finch is one of the most ingenious food getters of the bird world, though Darwin did not know this at the time. It uses a sharp stick to get insects out of a tree like a man uses a fork to get pickles out of a jar. When hungry, the perky finch flits through the low bushes of the island hunting for the perfect tool, a stick or

*The Darwin finch, with piercing stick*

cactus spine about an inch and a half long. Upon finding one, he tests it for length and strength. If it does not meet his requirements, he drops it and searches on. The right one secured, the bird takes it in his beak and flies to a tree, usually a dead stump, where he holds it in his feet while he drills into the bark after an insect. Lacking a long tongue that can snap up prey, the finch pokes his stick into the hole with his beak, spears the morsel, and draws it out of its chamber. Shifting the tool to his foot again he eats, then promptly takes the stick in his beak and continues the hunt and drilling.

Although a herring gull cannot be said to be a true tool user, it approaches this classification when it picks up a clam and, winging up into the air, drops it on the rocks to break it open. So innate is this behavior, so deeply is it embedded in inherited habits, that most sea gulls don't understand what they are doing. I have watched many pick up a clam, fly into the air, and drop it on sand over and over again, without getting the proper results. A sea gull I raised also possessed all the instincts of clam dropping, but none of the reasoning. When given a clam he would almost instantly carry it up in the air, circle my lawn, and drop it. One day I counted twenty-three attempts on his part to smash the clam before he gave up, alighting beside it and staring at it with one eye as if it contained some secret he had not quite figured out. Indeed, he had not. About ten feet from him lay a large rock garden.

Fish crows also drop clams, but they seem to know why they break. While walking along a Connecticut beach, I watched one of these wise birds soar into the sky and drop a clam on the beach. It did not break, but he did not try the beach again, instead he winged overhead until he spotted the macadam road. On this hard surface he met with success on the first try.

The force of gravity may not be a true implement, ingeniously used as it is, but the charming sea otter of the northern coach of California, like the Galapagos finch, is a true tool user. He deliberately picks up a rock with which to smash the hard-shelled abalones that make up the main part of his diet. An otter will dive, find a shell, and if it is too large and hard to bite open, he will swirl to the ocean floor again and pick up a flat rock. Pressing it to his chest, he rolls on his back and surfaces. With a bang and a clatter he breaks the abalone and picks out the delicate meat with his paws.

*Otter breaking a shell*

Shell smashing is limited to the sea otters of northern California where the abalones are abundant. The same species in Alaskan waters have never been observed to use a stone as a tool, perhaps because they feed primarily on the burrowing sea urchins. However, no one has gone down to watch how these intelligent mammals obtain their food. Perhaps, down among the dark rocks, they too use tools, for the burrowing sea urchin, a remarkable animal in its own right, is difficult to obtain. It bites its way into rocks, even steel piers, with no more than tiny calcium mouthparts. Once in its burrow, the urchin keeps grinding the stone, growing until eventually it can no longer exit or even be pulled out of its narrow entrance way. How, then, do the sea otters extricate them?

Occasionally individual animals or isolated groups of non–tool-using species will hit upon the idea of an implement to serve a need. A society of chimpanzees in the Gombe Game Preserve, Africa, hunt termites by poking sharp twigs into their burrows and impaling them. Not far from these animals along the Gombe Stream, individual chimps have been observed by primatologists, to blot up water from deep tree holes that they can't get their mouths into by dipping mashed leaves and using them to soak up the moisture. And one individual who certainly deserves special mention among tool users was observed to pick leaves and use them as toilet paper to clean itself after defecation.

Primatologists recently have discovered other monkeys who use eating tools. In the mountains of Japan, the macaque monkeys use water to separate dirt from grain. S. Kawamura, a Japanese primatologist who studied the macaque clan of Takasakiyama, sacred animals that are fed and protected by an order of monks, tell of a female who scoops up a handful of soy beans and rice, runs to the stream, and seating herself beside a pool, dumps her sandy ration in the water. The dirt sinks to the bottom, the grains float to the surface, and she gathers the cleaned grains to eat.

A few other monkeys observed her activities, figured out what she was doing, and now also wash grain, though others cannot quite get the idea. Of these, however, a few have figured out something else, and when the washers go to the stream to eat, the second-rate thinkers take up positions below them. The downstreamers have learned that grains escape the fingers of the washers and are carried on the water to them.

Some of these same monkeys wash potatoes to rid them of grit, a trick that was discovered by a little girl monkey who taught it to her playmates who taught it to their mothers. A joyful in-group of females then gathered together for potato washing.

From the University of Singapore comes word from young primatologist Mickey Chiang that the long-tailed macaques of the Singapore Botanical Gardens use leaves to pick up seeds and fruits that are lying on the dirty ground, then rub them clean in these natural washrags. On occasion they roll ant-filled fruit on the ground to rid it of the pests.

A delightful individual tool user is a captive Capuchin, a South American monkey, that lives in the London Zoo. He picks up a bone and cracks nuts with it. Tool using seems appropriate among apes and monkeys with their prehensile hands and close kinship to man, but what of a loggy old vulture who cracks an ostrich egg by throwing a stone at it? This is indeed a wonderment.

Several years ago Baroness Jane van Lawick-Goodall, Ph.D., and her husband, Baron Hugo van Lawick, were driving through Seregenti National Park in northern Tasmania. They brought their car to a sudden halt beside an open field for they could not believe what they were seeing. Two Egyptian vultures, white birds with golden cheeks and about the size of ravens, were standing before an ostrich egg. One of the birds had a stone in its beak. While the van Lawicks watched, the bird threw back its head, flipped its neck forward, and hurled the stone. It struck the egg with a whack. The vulture then walked up to it, saw that the shell had not broken, and picked up the stone again. The next pitch missed the egg entirely,

*The stone-throwing vulture*

but on the third try the shell cracked, and a few more hurls opened it. Hardly did the vultures bury their beaks in the yolk when they were driven off by larger vultures, the white-backed, hooded, and lappet-faced, who had been standing in a circle watching them. The big birds were not intelligent enough to learn from the Egyptians, but they did understand the consequences of their efforts and waited patiently for the feast.

A few Egyptians have learned to outwit the larger vultures. Two observed by the van Lawicks approached a deserted ostrich egg and, while one stood guard, the other hurled stones. With threats and cries, the guard drove off the parasites so that by the time the egg was broken the arena was clear for the Egyptians to dine undisturbed.

The Egyptian vultures are so motivated• that they threw stones at all spherical objects the van Lawicks presented them, real eggs, false eggs, big and small. The bigger the object the more excited they became, and several alighted too far away from these objects to be within striking distance of them, but tossed stones anyway.

The dining rooms of wild creatures are generally where the food is caught, but not always. Some carry their meals away to spots more appropriate for dining. The most breathtaking is the table of the swallow-tailed kite of Florida's Everglades. This bird is a glorious flier who swings through the sky on pointed wings and climbs high into the heavens far beyond man's vision. Dropping back toward earth, it pirouettes like a dancer. It seems fitting that this sky lover should choose the high winds for its place to eat.

After catching a snake, its favorite food, the kite flies up-ward until it meets a breeze upon which it can spread its wings and stand still in the air. There, hanging motionless in the sky, its tapered wings open, the bird leans down and daintily snips off tidbits of snake. I have never watched this performance without wanting to sing, for there is something about a bird that dines on a table of wind that lifts the spirits.

Like the mouthless Convolutas, the animals whose spoons are dances lingered in my mind long after the dinner at the Waldorf was over. Two years ago I found them in one of this land's most beautiful environments, a vernal pond tucked among hemlocks beside a great boulder in a New York forest not far from my home. The day was in March, snow still covered the ground, and the pond was black and patched with ice. As I stood on the rock looking down, I noticed bright colors in the water, and leaning over saw that the pond was astir with fairy shrimp, tiny branchipods that swim forever on their backs peering up at the spring skies through large black eyes. Rainbow-colored filaments streamed from their bodies like scarves as they darted and turned in the water. I was entranced, for fairy shrimp can only be found during the two weeks of each year that precede spring. After returning home I paged through a zoology book to learn more about them and discovered that at long last I had found the dancers of which the professor had spoken.

Along the margin of the body of the fairy shrimp are ten flaps that stand up like dividers in an index file. These are used for both swimming and feeding. Water runs over these flaps and flutters them in complicated combinations so that some close, others part, and still others fall wide open. The plankton-rich water is jetted across these by the dance of the shrimp. As they shoot forward, backward, and down, food catches in the flaps and drops inward toward the body of the shrimp where it is picked up by tiny filters. A shift in the shrimp's dance closes the flaps, and the food is shuttled up a groove lined with hair-like setules. These hairs whip it to the mouth where it strikes glands and stimulates them to excrete an adhesive material. The glue and food form a ball, which the shrimp picks up with its top jaw and shoves into its mouth. Marvelous!

Early the next morning I returned to the pond, and stretching out on a rock, watched with comprehension as the fairy shrimp danced while they ate. I saw them change directions to close their flaps, then swirl in another direction to send the food to their mouths. A gray-streaked sky hung over me, a flock of silent red-winged blackbirds moved north through the trees, and the seven-course meal at the Waldorf did indeed seem heavy-handed and unimaginative.

CHAPTER 8

# *STRANGE WORLDS THROUGH STRANGE SENSES*

MUSCLES can be measured and the tissues labeled, sex is determined, movement analyzed, and parents and offspring observed, but what an animal hears, sees, smells, and feels is at best an elusive science. We must use our senses to determine the senses of others, and here we are limited.

In man there are five senses: hearing, touch, sight, scent, and taste—the instruments with which we measure the environment. The eyes measure light and light patterns to give us shapes, the skin measures temperature and mechanical movements, while the ear measures the movements of the air. Chemical concentrations are evaluated through the tongue and nose. Anatomists have searched for other sense receptors but have found no more. The five senses are our windows to the world.

Yet we do have other senses, although we have no receptors for them. Thirst and hunger are examples. Of hunger physiologists simply say that it seems to come rhythmically at a certain stage of emptying the stomach. Thirst appears to involve stimulation, possibly in the hypothalamus, by dryness of the membranes of the pharynx, but scientists say there are no organs that can be labeled hunger and thirst receptors.

Through our own limited senses, the senses of the lower

animals become even more baffling. They receive messages from the environment with strange organs that hear voices we cannot hear, smell chemicals we cannot detect, and follow signals we know nothing about. Therefore it is difficult, perhaps impossible, to understand the stimuli that do not exist for us. Nevertheless, they are intriguing, and scientists have been able to describe some of the exotic senses of other creatures. They have experimented with stimuli and reactions and utilized modern equipment to record various kinds of sound and light undetectable through human senses. They have found that the world is a far different place to the lower forms of life than to us. By studying other animals they also know this—all man's senses can be rated good to excellent, but far inferior to the eyes of the hawk, the touch sense of the mole, the ears of the bat, the nose of the deer, the chemical sense of the catfish.

Humans are left out of a great range of possible experience. Knowledge concerning the most sensitive animals is limited to the work of those men whose interests have been piqued sufficiently to experiment, pry, and unlock the few secrets of the animal world that we do know. Outstanding among these secrets is that of the honey bee, and scientific priers have discovered that to a bee there is no daisy with white petals and gold center.

Beginning in the Thirties the bee came under intensive study in Germany in the lab of Karl von Frisch. He startled the scientific world in 1946 when he announced that bees have a language—a dance through which a forager bee can communicate to other bees the direction of and distance to a flower. When van Frisch demonstrated that bees indicated direction by using the polarized light of the sun, other scientists began to wonder what other lights a bee sees that we do not. By testing the reactions of these insects to various colors of the spectrum, investigators found that one of their visual attributes was the ability to see ultraviolet light. Given this information a photographer put an ultraviolet lens over his camera, took a picture of a daisy, and to his amazement saw that the tip of each petal glowed with a purple light, to create from a bee's point of view an illuminated landing field that marks off the pollen and nectar.

Further research into the vision of the bee transforms the garden from a place of leaves and flowers, paths and grass, to a sea on which lie flat broken forms, such as crosses and stars (open flowers). Compact designs—squares and circles (buds and leaves) do not exist to the bee. When given a choice of cutouts, they fly directly to the broken designs and ignore the

*What the honeybee sees*

compact forms, no matter how brilliantly colored they are. For good reason, bees are not interested in foodless buds or leaves.

As keen as this shape sense is, the world to bees on a calm day is practically a blank piece of paper, for they do not see well when the flowers are still. Like all insects they have rigid eyes that cannot move as ours do to bring objects into focus. Our sockets contain tiny muscles that constantly pull our eyes back and forth, up and down, in jerks and drifts to bring motion to still articles. Without this action, as demonstrated by experiments in which special contact lenses still the muscles, details blur and objects vanish. This explains why bees tend to stay in the hive on a calm day.

So in addition to, of course, light, it is primarily the wind that the bee depends upon for good vision, although the movement of its flight can also give some action to objects. When the blossoms bob and flowering limbs tremble, the bees pour from their hives and descend upon the dancing designs with instant accuracy, for they can see in all directions —down, behind, and to the sides with their big compound eyes, and upwords with the three simple eyes they have on top of the head.

Objects to a bee are not sensed through its eyes alone. In the antennae lie other receptors believed to be a combination of our senses of smell and taste. At least one function of these is to bring the bee home without using its eyes.

While the bees were out foraging a European experimenter moved the behive to a new location a short distance from the old one. When the bees returned they all gathered in the air at the spot where their front door had been. For five minutes they hung there, then turned and flew to the hive in its new location. A few days later the antennae were removed from many of the bees, and when they flew off to forage, the hive was moved once more. These bees did not come back to the old location, however, but flew directly to the hive. With the directional sense receptors in their antennae removed, they were forced to use their eyes to navigate.

Ever since I was a child I wondered what it would be like to see the world through the 12,000 eyes of the butterfly. Now it can be told. The thousands of eyes produce but one image on the retina and brain just like the pinpoints of light and dark on the TV set. But because each eye tapers into a common center, the compound eye magnifies everything, a necessity for a tiny beast who hunts food in a one- to two-inch garden—a flower.

A magnifying glass held inside a blossom gives some idea of the butterfly's view. The petals are enormous tent tops with rope-like veins of color running through them. The particles of pollen are yellow baseballs, and the tiny calyx is an enormous tunnel, lined with long-sized hairs that lead to a bucket of nectar. To the butterfly, the aphid in the flower is a hump-backed horse.

The world seen by the toad, an animal that also has eyes rigid in its head, is likewise blank until something moves. This was demonstrated by a Connecticut biologist who delved into the vision of these amphibians. He placed a lazy Susan with hamburger on it before a group of hungry toads. As long as the turntable was motionless, the toads did not eat, though the hamburger was within inches of their noses. At a twist of the wheel, however, they leaped, snatched the hamburger with their flashing tongues, and ate ravenously. Such eyesight is perfect for this beast whose brain is small and to whom an ant or fly would be quickly lost in the confusion of the many other things along a garden path or on a woodland floor. By seeing only things that move, the eye of the toad has little to divert it and can aim its tongue with deadly accuracy.

Three lenses in one explains the uncanny ability of the Atlantic flying fish to look through the water in the weed-filled Sargasso Sea, pick a point of emergence, scull his tail, take off, and then while flying through the air select a reentry point in one to fifteen seconds. This is quite a feat when the eye of the fish is understood. The cornea is usually rounded, an adaptation for focusing under water. When on land a fish is far-sighted. Land animals, on the other hand, have elliptical corneas, and when underwater they become near-sighted. The flying fish has adapted to both mediums by developing a low, three-sided pyramid with slightly bulging surfaces. It can look up and forward through the front face of the pyramid, up and backward through the rear face, or down through the bottom of the triangle. Thus it looks through flat windows instead of convex lenses. This gives undistorted vision under water as well as in the air; man would like to imitate this gimmick as he dives in and out of the sea.

Like most people who own dogs, I have often wondered what the house, the garden, and people look like to my pet. I was disappointed for her sake to learn that she did not see color but only shades of gray. The green lawn, the yellow buttercup, the red ribbon tied around her neck at Christmas are only charcoal images in her eyes. Only man and a few primates among the mammals see color. In the lower forms of life, the reptiles, birds, insects, fish, and octopi also enjoy the paint box of the spectrum, many of them seeing more of it than we see. Our slightly yellowish lenses absorb the ultra-violet, and of course infrared is not part of our experience.

Despite their lack of color vision, dogs can see greater distances than we—hand signals a mile away can be read by English sheep dogs. But it is the world of smells that is their rainbow. Not only can they follow the gamey tang of pheasant on the ground and in the air, and know that a puppy has passed their domain, but they can discern emotions such as fear and aggression in other animals. Recently it was shown that their own urine was a kind of marking paint. As almost everyone has observed, male dogs mark trees and posts. For years it was believed that these scents told other dogs who the marker was. In 1966 Devra Kleiman of the London Zoological Society ran scent tests on the canine family at the zoo and found that, more important, urine serves to distinguish the territory. A post marked by a fox, wolf, or dog stands out from the landscape for him, even at a distance; scent marking is a means of familiarizing an individual with its environment and reassuring it in unknown situations, a useful function indeed.

A songbird's view of the world is hard to imagine because it does not see whole objects, but just details. To a creature that travels swiftly and must therefore detect limbs, twigs,

*"Enemy" of the songbird*

enemies and prey instantly, this is a distinct advantage. Picking out a single detail is quicker than analyzing a whole bird, cat, hawk, or tree. David Lack of Oxford University, England, discovered that a bird sees only one detail when he placed in his yard a ball of red yarn on a stick and a stuffed robin whose breast was painted brown. Since male robins attack other male robins in their territory, the robin of Lack's yard attacked the yarn—which had no beak, eyes, wings, or feet— not the stuffed bird, which did. He concluded that the red breast and the red breast alone was a male robin to a robin. Such a detail he called a "releaser" (Lack's use of the word "releaser" came from the scientist Konrad Lorenz). This object triggers reaction. Since that memorable day in Lack's yard, other releasers have been discovered in songbirds. A "hawk or owl" to these birds is a cross, the short top the releaser. When cardboard crosses were flown, short end first over caged songbirds, they called in alarm and hid, but when stuffed owls were flown backwards over them these elicited no reaction. Moving backward the long tail says "goose or heron," and such a bird is not an enemy.

Just what detail says "man" to a bird has not been studied, but whatever they see, it is so specific that a bird can recognize an individual. When a pair of robins in the front yard of a Michigan farm were live-trapped and banded by a friend of mine, the birds fought and cried in terror. When, in addition, their young were removed from the nest and also given bands, the adults almost went into shock. Apparently the combination of experiences was so traumatic that the birds were forever conditioned to recognize some mysterious detail on the bander. Every time he walked through the yard he was attacked. Other people, both men and women, could pass without arousing the robins. He alone they dive-bombed and struck with their wings, even the following year when they returned from migration, and even when he dressed in other clothing. One day, however, the bander drove under the nest on a tractor, and the robins did not even chirp. Then he dismounted, and once more they screamed and dove at him. By sitting on the tractor some detail had changed—which, he still does not know, perhaps his two legs, perhaps his stride, perhaps the curve of his spine.

The markings on nestling birds further verifies the fact that birds see only details. Most babies have bright red mouths that are rimmed with yellow. When open they make a perfect target, a releaser that sets off the feeding behavior in the adults and directs the food to the object. As the nestlings grow, these colors fade and as they do, the attentions of the parents fade also.

The scent receptors in all but one or two species of birds are less keen than ours, their windows to the world being almost entirely visual. So keen are their eyes that some can read attitudes in men that we cannot. The crow is uncanny in this respect.

Every farmer knows that when he approaches them with a gun, crows get on their wings and vanish, returning later to ravish his crops. Years ago a government crow expect, E. R. Kalmbach, ran an experiment to see if he could help farmers with this problem by disguising himself in a long skirt and bonnet and camouflaging his gun in a broomstick. In this costume he went crow hunting. The birds took one look at him as he got out of his car and departed. When, however, in this same disguise he walked into the field without a gun hidden in the broom the crows went on eating. He could only conclude that when a man carries a gun he unconsciously displays some aggressive attitude that the crows recognize. He suggested that farmers try changing their attitudes.

Even more astonishing is the crow sense that recognizes and speaks of death. In the state of Washington several years ago, a farmer, endeavoring to rid his almond plantation of thousands of crows, tried everything from poisoned grain, smoke, and gun blasts to the clanking of tin cans—to no avail. Finally he struck upon the idea of soaking almonds in strychnine. Two crows ate them and dropped dead. Within minutes a sad sound was passed through the trees, a signal that was apparently a word of death. Thousands of crows took to their wings, and arising like a black thunderhead, winged over the almond trees and out of sight over the horizon, the talk of death still moaning through the flock. They never ret··rned.

The vision of day-prowling snakes has recently come to man's attention; it is now realized that for millions of years they have been wearing the yellow Novoil lenses that give skiers and hunters acute vision in bright sunlight. The "goggles" or lenses of these snakes are also yellow, and like Novoil absorb the violet end of the spectrum, cut out unequal refraction, and enhance sight. Having figured out in our brain what the snakes had achieved by inheritance, we can now see as clearly in strong light as they. As yet we have not perfected the other miraculous eye of the snakes—the eye that sees warm bodies in the dark. This receptor is still a mystery. It lies in the head somewhat below the eyes and above the nostrils of certain species—pit vipers, rattlesnakes, copperheads, and water moccasins—and is actually two conical pits lined with sensory cells, hence their name. A miraculous organ, it is sensitive to the radiant heat or infrared light from warm bodies, whether they are a balloon filled with tepid water or a flying bat. Until recently even the function of the pit was unknown and today its "how" still belongs to the snakes. Some scientists, however, believe that the two pits see and focus on radiant heat in a way that is something like our eyes seeing and focusing on lighted objects.

Only such a sense could explain how the Cuban boa, a snake that lives in the dark caves of Trinidad, can catch flying bats in pitch blackness. To this gifted animal, bats would be low red lights, something like the hot coil of an electric stove, weaving and darting in space. The caves of the snakes are probably different to them than to us. Through receptors, the boas "listen" to vibrations and are guided over cold rocks and away from sheer cliffs and deep pools. Theirs must be a weirdly beautiful world: the sounds and taste of precipices, of dampness, and still water—choruses we will never hear.

Our hearing is so poor that for ages the bat was a witch that maneuvered in the night around walls, twigs, and door-ways with sightless eyes. It was not until 1937 that a scientist suspected and proved that the bats' travel through darkness had something to do with sound. In that year a young Harvard senior, Donald R. Griffin (presently with the Rockefeller Institute), enthralled with the unerring piloting of bats, read that in 1793 an Italian scientist, Lazaro Spallanzani, had plugged the ears of some bats and observed that they struck walls and door. Griffin ran similar experiments, but it was not until he gathered enough courage to approach the renowned physicist, George W. Pierce, who had invented a parabolic horn that brought the voices of insects down to human hearing levels, that Griffin proved bats had voices we cannot hear. Courage in hand, he knocked on Pierce's laboratory door and explained to the elderly man that he wished to put his bats in front of his horn. Eagerly the professor invited him in, and that morning man heard for the first time the supersonic voices of the bats. After several years of further research, Griffin was able to prove that the bats, furthermore, bounced these sounds off trees, branches, and insects to maneuver in the darkness by echoes from their own voices. With that the image of the bat changed from ancient witchery to the modern wizardry of echo location.

Griffin's latest research demonstrates that bats also project their dominance and subdominance, and set up and maintain their society through sound. Such a world would be like our listening to a tape recording of a symphony orchestra and knowing by the sounds from the individual players how many men and women were in the orchestra, who dominated whom, as well as who was old and who was young.

Exactly how bats estimate range is still a mystery, although J. D. Pye of the University of London's King College has shown through high-speed photography that rapid ear movements are closely correlated to the production of signals used for echo location. Some scientist suggests that this indicates the two ears act as eyes and find an object by triangulation.

Penguins were also suspected of being sonar experts in 1963. A group of zoologists at a members' meeting of the San Francisco Zoological Society ambled over to the penguins at dusk and were fascinated to see them rapidly catch scattered fish in their tank, although it was almost dark. The men suspected that they might, like porpoises, send out beeps, and within a few days arrangements were made to send four Humboldt penguins to the Stanford Research Center for study. The birds were put in an anechoic tank, a pool with walls constructed to absorb sound and prevent echoes from the sides from interfering with other sounds. T. C. Poulter took on the assignment, threw two fish into the water, and turned out the lights as the birds dived. In the darkness he scattered other fish, and when the lights went on in thirty seconds all the fish had been eaten. This was proof enough for Poulter that penguins use some kind of sonar for locating food. He did not understand how, because instruments showed that the birds emitted no sounds either sonic or ultrasonic.

Fur seals, also suspected of using a type of sonar, were tested in the anechoic tank, and they too picked up fish in the darkness without emitting beeps. Sounds, however, were recorded—a series of strange clicks that seemed to have a physical rather than animal source. In 1969 Poulter discovered what the penguins and fur seals were listening to—cavitation clicks produced by the collapse of cavities that are formed in the water when they swim. The cavities are about a millimeter in diameter and are created by the rapid movement of penguins and seals. As they travel in all directions from the vicinity of the penguin's or seal's body, the clicks reach its ears and register the time of departure of the outgoing sound. Echoes returning from the fish tell the predators where the fish are located, something a man might be able to do if he could swim rapidly enough.

Also perplexing has been the hearing sense of some species of owl which can catch mice in pitch blackness without emitting sounds, without turbulence cavities, and with no sense of smell or eyesight for heat. It has long been known that owls have asymmetrical ears, one ear opening higher than the other, and Roger S. Payne of Cornell, believing that this had something to do with their ability to catch food in the dark, ran a series of experiments with a barn owl. He took movies of the bird striking a mouse-sized wad of paper in light and darkness (a light-tight cage) and confirmed the suspicion that owls used their ears to catch food. In the blackness the bird could not use his vision, the paper had no heat that could direct the owl by means of infrared sensitivity, and no odor. The films of the bird hunting in blackness were taken with a sniperscope camera (a device like the snake's pit which transforms invisible infrared light into visible light). The films showed that when the owl struck in darkness it did not glide, raise its wings just before striking, throw its feet forward, its head back, and close its eys on impact as it did in daylight; it flapped violently to the mouse swinging its feet back and forth until, over its prey, the owl brought its talons forward, threw its head back, and struck. All this did not mean much until Payne noticed that one action was similar in both light and darkness. The owl while still on the perch turned its head toward the mouse, oriented itself, and took off.

After testing the owl's ears, Payne found that sounds in the owl's right ear occur about ten to fifteen degrees higher than their complements for the left ear. This diversity, which is likened to the asymmetry of the ears, makes sound decrease with extreme rapidity in one ear while it decreases with extreme slowness or even increases in the other. When the owl tried to match intensities in his two ears, differences due to incorrect orientation of the head are amplified. But when the bird orients its head in such a way as to hear all frequencies at a maximum intensity in both ears, it is automatically facing the source of sound. Lined up with the mouse through a balance of sounds achieved by swinging its head and even whole body from side to side, the owl flies, approaches, and throws back its head. Its feet aligned with the sound, the owl strikes! The accuracy is almost infallible—less than one degree.

Just two years ago another strange sense of the birds was demonstrated—the olfactory prowess of the kiwi, that marvelous flightless bird of New Zealand. It can smell worms underground.

Bernice M. Wenzel of the University of California tested five of these long-beaked birds during a three months' visit to the Mount Bruce Native Bird Reserve, New Zealand in 1968, and discovered that although most birds have a poor sense of smell, the kiwi does not. Not only are the bird's olfactory bulbs larger compared with the rest of the forebrain than those of all other birds, but it is the only bird that has nostrils at the tip of the beak rather than close to the head, a positioning that led scientists to suspect that the kiwi sniffed worms.

Miss Wenzel proved this by placing foreign odorants on small pieces of cotton at the bottom of three glass tubes. Three other tubes were not scented. The birds always went to those with odor ignoring the others. To test them further, Miss Wenzel put food in several pots and covered them with dirt. Control pots of dirt with no food were also made available to the birds as well as one pot in which she put a large juicy earthworm and covered it with two to three inches of soil. All the food pots were broken into in every test, none of the pots without food were broken into. Many holes were poked in the earthworm pot and the worm was gone in the morning. So it is true that these shy wingless birds with their shrill piping voices that earned them the name kiwi do inded smell worms

*How the kiwi smells its food*

two to three inches under the ground and probe down to them with long sensitive sniffers.

Perhaps the most valuable sense of the lower animals in the Atomic Age is their awareness of X-rays, a gift that sends them away from these lethal rays and even changes their habits when struck with it. A team of scientists, led by Dale Morris of the Argonne National Laboratory in Argonne, Illinois, believes that the aversive stimulus is one product of a peroxide action of catalase, an enzyme in the blood. Just what the chemical nature of it is unknown; they only know that they have a mutant mouse that cannot detect X-ray and its catalase is different from the others' catalase.

The way in which sensitivity to X-ray has been detected is fascinating. While under an X-ray machine, mice are given saccharine water to drink and thereafter they will avoid it, for they associate the sweet water with the pain, the misery—whatever it is they feel under X-ray. When returned to their cages or when placed under radiation again and given a choice of waters, they refuse the saccharine water as if it were the plague.

The mice that don't sense X-rays are of interest to the Atomic Energy Commission, for by studying what they don't have, the enzyme in normal animals might be isolated and produced. Men might someday sense these lethal rays in the atmosphere and so move out of the line of fire to avoid unseen and unfelt damage—even death.

We rarely pause to think about gravity, as we automatically keep ourselves balanced with a mechanical device in our inner ears. In each is a set of three sacs that contain tiny crystals of lime suspended in fluid. When this fluid is shifted in the semi-circular canals, we "sense" that we are off balance and right ourselves. Were we, however, to lose this lime and fluid, few of us would be aware that they were missing or how to replace them. Yet the lowly shrimps and lobsters not only know what makes their sense of gravity work, but how to repair it when it does not.

On either side of the heads of these animals are little boxes that lie at the base of the antennae and open to the outside through small pores. As the animals move through the water, sand seeps into the pores and collects on the bottom of the boxes. When the crayfish or lobster goes up or down, the sand tilts and tells him how he is aligned with the pull of the earth's gravity. He rights himself, the sand levels out, and he is at one with the force. However, each time a shrimp or lobster molts its skin, the sand is shed with the chitin covering. Usually the sea water seeps in through the pore and deposits silt again, but if not, the animal will stick its head into the sand and replenish the supply or—marvelously—fill the boxes by picking up sand in its claws and dropping it through the holes.

A shrimp, kept in a tank of sterile, sandless water, shed its carapace and consequently its sand, stood on it head, side, and back as it floundered like a drunken man. When it was totally confused, the experimenters placed tiny iron filings in the water, and the shrimp not only staggered to them, but picked them up in its claws and put them in its boxes. That these are the balancing organs of the shrimp was proved beyond a doubt when the zoologist held an electromagnet over the animal's head. The shrimp turned on its back for the pull was greater than the force of gravity, and the top of the tank became the bottom to the animal.

Shrimp and lobsters have other sensory organs that scientists have not yet explained—the bristles that cover their antennae and bodies. Fifty thousand of these receptors project from their legs and feet alone, receiving messages about the force and direction of water currents, the voices of other sea animals, and the whereabouts of food. It is difficult to imagine shopping for food through the hairs of our bodies.

It is the sense receptors of the common dog tick, however, that baffles scientists even more. This animal not only detects warm bodies, but cold ones. So keen is the thermal sense of the tick that it has no eyes and doesn't need them. When it hatches, this arachnid lacks legs and sex organs and is more like an instrument than a beast. In this stage, it is attuned only to cold-blooded animals like lizards and frogs. Born on the tip of a grass blade, having no way to move or hunt, it simply waits for chance to bring an amphibian or reptile within its range. Months can pass before that cold message reaches the tick and stimulates it to fall, then bite. Having secured the blood of a frog it grows, sheds its skin several times, and acquires legs and sex organs. Able to creep it moves in its own darkness to find a member of the opposite sex and mate. The male then dies, and the female starts off on a completely different hunt—a search for a warm-blooded animal which gives off a substance called butyric acid, to which the tick is highly sensitive.

The female picks up weak sources of this acid on animal

trails and climbs to the top of a grass blade. She is aware of which direction is up by the light impulses that she receives through photosensitive cells (not eyes) which are primitive organs that respond to light and darkness. Above the trail she waits for days, months, even years, until strong fumes of butyric acid envelop her. When the intensity of the acid is exactly right she releases her grip on the blade and falls onto the back of a warm-blooded animal, burrows down through the fur and bites into the skin. She gorges on the blood. This meal to her is nothing more than a warm fluid, for experimental ticks provided with water of the right temperature have gorged themselves on this. When replete, the tick drops to the ground, climbs a glass blade, and lays her eggs without having known any more of this earth than temperature, butyric acid, and a feeble glow that comes from above.

As dull as a fish's world might seem to a man, it is nevertheless filled with wild and wonderful sensations that we cannot imagine. Like snakes, fish have no outer ear, and the inner ear seems out of contact with all possible water sounds, for it is buried in the bones of the skull. Furthermore, the fish have no cochlea, that organ concerned with analyzing pitch in reception of sound. So for years it was assumed that fish could not hear.

Several years ago a German physiologist experimented with the European minnow and one of the common catfishes of that country. He removed the inner ear and the reactions of the fish to sound dropped so enormously that he realized they did hear through their ears. Other studies indicate that the fish with the keenest hearing are those whose inner ears are connected to their air bladders. Eels, goldfish, and weakfish receive warning vibrations through their bodies which are amplified by the air bladders. These fish flee from sound with a more violent action than those that have no such connection.

Another organ of hearing in the fish is the lateral line, that dark line that runs down the side. Under this is a tube filled with mucus. The tube opens to the outside through pores and beneath it runs a nerve that branches. The branches end in sensory organs. When this tube is removed, the fish performs perfectly normally except in one respect. It does not respond to low frequency vibrations in water, and so it seems that it is the lateral line, plus the ears, plus (in some instances) the air bladder that bring the sound of the sea and stream to the consciousness of the fish. Since they live in water where vibrations are water ripples that actually touch the fish, sounds are more like "feel" than the noises we hear. To a minnow, the stir of a bass or a catfish upstream is as if your back door opened when you were upstairs and you could touch the milkman entering the house.

The lateral line of the fish measures one more part of the environment—the temperature. Since they are cold-blooded and take on the temperature of the water around them, these animals cannot adjust immediately to a change of temperature of even a few degrees, but must give their bodies time to warm up or cool off. To help them adjust, the lateral line takes the temperature of both fish and environment and somehow signals the beast not to travel from one temperature to another so fast that it will die as a result.

Of all wondrous fish, the catfish wins the prize for senses. Not only does it feel/hear its way through night waters with its inner ear and lateral line, but it finds food through a sense of smell/taste. This is the only way to describe the receptors that cover every fraction of its body. Protruding from its chin are whiskers and barbels that are auxiliary tongues rich in taste buds which react to chemicals like our nose and mouth. In addition, the almost scaleless skin of the catfish also tastes/smells, for every part—tail, side, fins, belly—acts as a tongue/nose.

On a summer afternoon, having caught a channel cat in

*Catfish tasting with its tail*

the Potomac River, I put it in a half-submerged rowboat, opened my sandwich bag, and began to eat my lunch while I waited for my father and brothers to come back from an island trip. Time dragged heavily and to amuse myself I decided to share my sandwich with the catfish. He snapped it up. The second piece, however, struck his tail, and without hesitating he turned and swallowed this, something I had never seen a fish do. Most have to see their food or wait several seconds until the odor travels to their noses. I was intrigued and dropped pieces that settled on his fins, back and whiskers.

No matter where the food touched him the old cat tasted, swirled, and swallowed. To find out if he was reacting to the touch, I also dropped pebbles on him. He did not rise to these. From that day to this, a stream or lake has been a different place to me—not an odorless world where I would not dare to sniff or open my mouth, but an ice cream parlor of flavors that the catfish taste/smell.

Some flavors are received by a fish in the nostrils, which are not attached to their trachea as are ours, but to a cavity in the head that is lined with measuring instruments that evaluate the chemicals of the water. The cavity, however, has no opening inside the body and must send its impulses along channels different from ours.

Another remarkable ability of some animals is in "sensing" water. Of these, the red flying frog of Sumatra, a great jumper, is the most uncanny. The female can locate small puddles no bigger than a dinner plate, ten to twelve feet below her and in the dark of the jungle night. When ready to lay eggs, the female climbs through the limbs of trees until she smells? tastes? sees? feels? hears? (not even herpetologist Wayne King at the Bronx Zoo in New York would guess) a protected pool of water far below her. She is so positive of her find that she lays a mass of foamy eggs on the branch directly above the puddle and departs. Within a few days the eggs hatch and the tadpoles, which must grow up in water or die, fall twelve feet from the limb and land in the pool. They never miss.

The animals that find water below ground always seemed mysterious to me until the summer I spent in the North American desert. After I had mentioned my wonderment to a geologist just as we approached a depression in a valley of the Arizona Sonoran Desert he told me to lean down and smell the soil. As I did, I smelled dampness on the dry air. Water, I realized, does have an odor. Deer, goats, lions, dogs—all the animals with a keener sense of odor than mine—could "smell" and dig down to unseen waters. But this experiment will never explain the red flying frog to me, for she senses a puddle in a moist world where everything smells of water.

Quite a few insects respond to moisture and can measure the humidity of the air with such precision that by watching their behavior an entomologist can predict a summer storm. The tsetse fly of Africa waits to lay its eggs until the atmosphere has reached the saturation point. Then, she lays quickly as the storm breaks, she ends abruptly, and the fly waits for the next build-up in humidity.

In our own country the stable fly viciously attacks and bites people or horses at the approach of a thunderstorm, so I learned from my father when he predicted almost to the minute the arrival of a distant storm by the intensity of a stable fly's bite.

For the most part we can understand the sense of touch in other animals, for we have sensitive fingers that relay to us delicate shapes, temperature, textures, and sizes. All parts of our body, of course, respond to touch. When contact is a directing factor, a pleasure, a need, it is called thigmotaxis. This sense takes strange forms in some insects. Honey bees for the most part work alone as they perform the endless jobs of the hive, but when ready to swarm, an inhibitor is turned off, a signal "to contact" goes on, and they pile one upon the other by the hundreds and thousands to fly en masse to a new home.

Baffling, and at the same time amusing, is the reaction to touch of the aphid, which feeds on the Helianthus, a sunflower. These little insects always sit up in a row along the stems and leaves. They feed and travel in a line; they also react to thigmotaxis in a line. If one of them is touched, even by the tip of a petal, it touches the next aphid, who passes the sensation to the next, until the whole line moves like a wave up and down the stem. Why do these aphids react like this? It does not seem to protect them from enemies nor is it related to sex or food getting. The best answer is simply that when touched, they touch.

As our sense of touch depends upon direct contact, it has never occurred to us that we might feel objects in any other way—but it has to the whirligig beetles (*Gyrinidae*), those flat swimmers that spin and dart across the surfaces of ponds and streams.

While swimming they either make no waves at all or very conspicuous circular and V-shaped patterns; these are their "fingers." The waves precede the beetle for several body lengths, strike objects, and send back echo waves that tell the insect to steer another course. Since the beetles travel so rapidly, this is a highly desirable arrangement to avoid collision.

A curious fact about the forewaves is that they are several times longer than the beetle's body length. Man's ships cannot make waves of such proportionate length. Furthermore, the speed at which the beetles travel should lift their bows off the water as it does a motorboat, but by creating waves compact and high, the beetles lie flat at all times.

Often the whirligigs will send out waves in many directions by jerking their bodies. These waves have centers at different points and report conditions from various directions along the beetle's path. Like other echo-locating devices in animals, it is believed that the waves also serve as a communications system between beetles.

The whirligig has still another remarkable device—its fantastic eyes. Although it appears to have two eyes, it actually has four. A horizontal line of tissue divides each eye across the middle. The lower part can look down into the water for enemies, while the upper part looks up into the air. Each half is specifically adapted to its own medium—air or water. For a surface dweller this is a perfect arrangement.

Of all reactions to environment, the one we least under-

*Amazing forewaves of the whirligig*

stand but most admire is the migration of the birds. The sun, the atmosphere, the temperature, the stars, all seem to speak to them, according to many scientific studies that have been made. What guides they follow depends on the species. Each August as I watch the swallows gather over the Hudson River to wait for some signal that will send them south to their wintering grounds, I am always intrigued and astounded when one day I see thousands, the next not one.

Temperature is at least one of the environmental stimuli that starts the birds off. Margaret Nice, the indefatigable ornithologist who has studied the life history of the song sparrow for many years, has published the most detailed and monumental record in existence on one type of bird: "Studies in the Life History of the Song Sparrow." She kept yearly temperature readings in fall. Cold snaps, she found, usually turn on the physiological clocks of migration. Once set, the clocks ticked on until the final alarm went off, sending the birds on their way. She came to this conclusion because some individuals had thresholds of temperature tolerance lower than others. They did not migrate if the autumns were warm, but stayed on to become that delight of man, the winter bird. However, these same banded birds in a colder autumn took off with the rest and migrated.

The declining hours of daylight are also a factor that triggers migration in fall. Starlings can be forced into the restless behavior of migration before their usual time by shortening their days artificially. And they can be brought into breeding plumage early by gradually lengthening their daylight in winter. Light and temperature are certainly two of the signals, but there are probably more.

Whatever the stimuli, there is no migratory flight to compare with that of the Arctic tern, a seemingly fragile bird that looks like a well-trimmed paper airplane with black cap and red cowling. It has the longest flight, and strangely, the young leave first, without any schooling from their elders. When the cold winds rise at the end of July on the barren Arctic tundra of Europe, Asia, and North America, the young terns grow restless. The signals heard, they leave their parents and strike out across the earth for the Antarctic, a ten thousand-mile trip to an unknown spot in the extreme southern Atlantic and Pacific, and this they find without having been there before.

Their course is not only long, but extremely complicated. The Arctic terns that nest in eastern North America cross the Atlantic from west to east, but avoid the warm waters of the western Atlantic for reasons unknown. Upon arriving above the shores of Europe, they turn and follow that coast south to Africa, until it vanishes into the South Atlantic Ocean. Here the young birds fly south crossing unmarked waters (as far as we know) to the tip of South America. Straight on south they go, across the vast windy home of the wandering albatross to finally find the Antarctic ice pack that is their winter home.

Alaskan terns, to make things more complicated, follow a different route. They take the Pacific Coast of North America to South America and from the tip of that continent take off across the wilderness of water to the Antarctic. When the young of both species are well on their way, the adults follow.

It would seem that once this trip was made, the way back in spring would be simple, but the Arctic tern does not even give itself this relief, for it returns by another route. Most follow the eastern coasts of South and North America as they come back to their breeding grounds.

As magnificently streamlined as the tern is, its flight seems ill-adapted to the long journey, for it never moves resolutely in a straight line as the plovers and other birds do, but rather it flutters and turns erratically in the wind, a flight that should exhaust it.

Of the distances the terns cover, information obtained from banding reveals one record that stands out above all others. An Arctic tern banded in western Greenland on July 8, 1951 was recovered on October 30, 1951 in Durban Harbor, Natal, South Africa. In 114 days the bird had covered eleven thousand miles, almost one hundred miles a day, and it still had not reached its destination. Incomplete as its journey was, that data from the white bird of Durban Harbor is the travel record for all the migrant birds that ornithologists have clocked.

The keen eyes of the birds serve them well in migration. Most of them follow rivers, coastal lines, or ranges of mountains. In North America these bird routes are well enough defined to be given geographical names: the Atlantic and Pacific Coastal Flyways, the Mississippi, and the Great Plains-Rocky Mountain route. Not all birds use these; tanagers, orioles, thrushes, and sparrows move over the continent on a broad front above seemingly unmarked terrain.

What do they sense? Observations show that some birds that fly by night use the stars as guideposts—the grosbeak, red-eyed vireo, great crested flycatcher, to mention a few, come to earth when the sky is cloudy and the stars are not visible.

Daytime migrants like the blackbird, robin, barn swallow, and chimney swift make use of the sun. Gustav Kramer of Heidelberg, Germany, placed starlings in a pavilion with six windows that could be darkened by movable shutters. Mirrors could direct sun rays at definite angles. When all the windows were open, the birds faced north-west during their spring migratory period. When the windows were closed and the position of the sun changed by mirrors, the starlings changed their direction to face what would be north-west if the mirror were the sun. Kramer found that each day birds could project the whole curve of the sun and stay on course at any moment of the day. As they fly they keep track of the sun's position and make the necessary corrections to remain oriented. They perform this remarkable feat through what Kramer called "a perfectly regulated internal clock." The workings of the mechanism are still theoretical, even today. After sixty years of sophisticated research we still know practically nothing about "how" birds get their bearings.

Birds also use the wind in migration, preferring to fly against it if possible; on a calm day they do not go at all.

Through the eyes and to some extent the senses of smell and touch, the demure and solitary African migratory locust is turned into a traveling demon. It changes color and shape. It is in the solitary phase one day, the migratory phase the next. During the latter, it can eat the equivalent of its weight in food each day, and multiply by the millions. The transformation takes place in twenty-four to forty-eight hours and is one of the most remarkable phenomena in nature. It is primarily induced by mere sight of other migratory locusts, a stimulus that transforms a loner that does not care to move much into a gregarious animal that is smaller, darker in color,

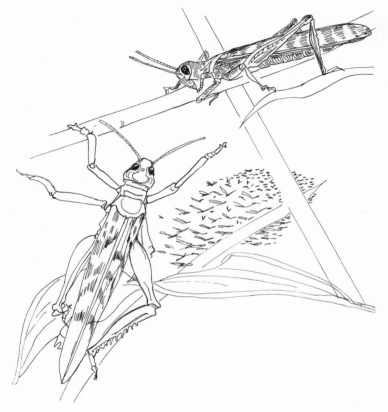

*Miracle of the migratory locust*

and must move great distances. Once changed, the migrants will build up their numbers to between 35 and 70 million individuals. They will cover thousands of square miles and devour 80,000 tons of food a day, enough to feed 400,000 people for a year. The last great outbreak of this locust in 1958 destroyed 167,000 tons of cereals in Ethiopia, enough to feed one million people for a year.

The transformation can be induced by entomologists by simply putting a locust in its solitary phase into a cage with others of its kind. Crowded together, the sight of others stimulates a hormone that shrivels them all into tiny monsters. The reverse is also true. A gregarious locust taken out of a swarm and put into isolation grows larger and paler until he has turned back into the docile insect of the solitary phase.

In the migrant phase when the air is still, locusts fly by night quite slowly for about thirty minutes on a straight course, then come down to rest. During the day some march forward on the ground and millions of eggs are laid. They hatch and mature in a few short hours to swell the ranks and create more locusts who create more locusts, until a plague is upon the land.

One such plague that began in Niger in mid-October 1967 was spotted from the air by entomologists who recognized the early stages of congregating—that seeing-each-other period that triggers the hormonal change. They recognize it because during this time the locusts roost, bask, feed, and hide, behavior that a trained eye can detect from the air. Consequently this first-stage outbreak in Niger was sprayed with insecticides, and, numbers reduced, the locusts changed back into their solitary phase. The plague was checked.

The migratory locust, contrary to belief, is not the locust of the Bible that was sent as a plague to Egypt. That insect is the desert locust which is still a danger in that country. It is a different species than the migratory locust and its life history has not yet been worked out. Consequently, Egypt is still ravaged by the desert locust despite the fact that more money has been spent in research on this insect than any other, including the disease-carrying mosquito.

Of all the voices from the environment that whisper to the sense receptors of animals, the most beautiful to me are those that tell the grizzly bear when to hibernate. As the air chills in autumn and the edges of the clouds grow soft with snow crystals, I try to feel the lowering pressure, the severity of the air, the crispness of grass blades that might tell me what they tell the bears—that tomorrow snow will blow over the land and not thaw until spring. I always wait for a phone call from my brothers Drs. John and Frank Craighead, who have studied the grizzly of Yellowstone for over ten years.

Anytime between October 1 to mid-November the phone will ring and John's voice will come in from the lab in Wyoming. "Ignore the calendar. Today is winter!" he announces. "The bears have gone to bed."

My brothers were among the first to employ the new space science of biotelemetry, gathering distant information on animals through radio transmitters and receivers. Since bears wander far into inaccessible country and are most active at night, no man could follow or consistently observe these North American wonders until this technique was developed.

Even with biotelemetry, facts are not easy to get. The bears have to be trapped, anesthetized, and color-tagged for identification by snapping numbered plastic tags of different colors into each ear. Then the enormous animals have to be weighed, measured, sexed, and fitted with collars carrying transmitters that will pulse at different rates for each individual.

Every autumn at least four were tracked to their dens, lonely rendezvous high on canyon walls with northern exposures, and it was these bears that gave my brothers the first insight into the miraculous sense receptors of the grizzlies. They all, John and Frank discovered, react to the same stimuli, for all hibernate on the same day. Over several years, they tried to discover the signals that the Yellowstone grizzlies heard.

They found the final trigger on November 11, 1965, when a storm rode into Yellowstone. Frank flipped on a receiver to hear erratic beeps coming from bear radios. One was giving the weak signal that meant that the bear had denned and that the radio was underground. However, the bear numbered 202 was sending a signal some distance from his den and Frank set out to find him. As he made his way for six miles through dense timber, he watched the ground for bear tracks. His receiver was telling him that 202 was nearby. He could not find him nor his footprints.

Suddenly he came upon 202 moving rapidly toward his den. Now Frank was certain of the one thing that the bears had been waiting for—a drifting blowing storm that would cover their tracks as they strode to their dens. In the morning there was not one grizzly track to tell which way the bears had gone.

When Frank went over his records and notes he found earlier environmental stimuli. A cold snap on September 15 had set off the first bell of hibernation, and the bears became drowsy. A month later the second signal came, possibly from the drowsiness itself—the urge to be alone. Slowly, like old men at the end of the day, the bears dragged off to their den sites. However, they did not den but waited with heads drooping, bodies reeling, for almost another month. On November 11, they heard the final message from the earth— the particular storm unlike all others before it that would not thaw but would lock up the plateau and cover the land until spring.

# CHAPTER 9

# REMARKABLE DECEIT
# AND AGGRESSION

EVERY animal, from the amoeba with its simple contract-release action to human beings with our bristling artillery and missiles, protects itself from enemies in some manner. The love of life is great among all. Protection and defense, however, was not a subject that aroused my interest until a day in Teton National Park. Resting along a trail to the Snake River, I noticed a piece of pine bark on the side of a tree fall up, not down, and getting to my feet, I found nothing to explain this. Suspecting, however, that it was some insect, I tapped the spot where it had seemed to alight. Nothing stirred. Finally, I blew. A long antenna moved and a pine sawyer beetle took shape, then stepped to the right, lined up with a protuberance of bark, and disappeared again. This time I knew where he was, picked up the piece of bark, and placed on my hand a splendid beetle with long wings and antennae and a back of gray mottled brown. It remained there only a moment. Out of its hiding place it hastily took to its wings, avoided a reddish-brown western hemlock, and alighted on another gray-brown pine where it disappeared again. I knew I was involved in one of the most bizarre aspects of nature, not a creature of flight and aggression but one of trick and deceit.

No biologist has given me a satisfactory answer as to how this camouflage comes about except to say that through natural selection, over ages past, those pine sawyer beetles that matched the bark were not eaten by their enemies and went on to produce young in their likeness.

This explanation will do for the pine sawyer beetle as well as the more famous Kallima butterfly of India that precisely resembles a dead leaf when its wings are folded, even to the veins and the leaf rib line down the middle. This insect rests only on vines and bushes that shed dead leaves during the growing season.

Natural selection also explains the odd Sargasso fish that resembles the Sargasso seaweed of the mid-Atlantic—down to its barbels, color, and mitten-shaped leaves. But it in no way explains the moth *Stenoma algidella*. This moth exactly resembles a bird dropping. Grayish white, it is slightly curled, with one end deeply stained with a grayish black mark. So real is the imitation as it rests on an apple leaf, that even my daughter recoiled from one when she was climbing the apple tree.

As I look at these moths each spring, the natural selection theory seems too chancy. Something in the tissue of that animal *knows* that bird droppings are not acceptable food to birds that eat moths. Since no one will accept my theory, I settle for the fact that they are scientifically called "imitators," a name sufficiently revealing.

Among the imitators are caterpillars whose backs are shaped like the edge of the leaf they are eating, complete to serrations and lobes, depending upon the plant species, and a moth of a new, yet unnamed genus found near Ocalaria, Panama, that itself does not copy, but throws a shadow that does. When they rest on a tree, these moths hang head up in the light in such a way that their bodies throw black triangular shadows that resemble thorns. The eye instantly looks at the dark spot, not the pale creature above. These moths sit in scattered

*Weevil with its garden on its back*

groups, making the tree look as if it were covered with sharp, black thorns.

An enchanting clue to the colors came from the zoology and botany labs of the University of London in the spring of 1970. The yellows, reds, and blues of butterflies come from the pigments in the plants they eat while in the caterpillar stage. The blue of the common blue butterfly matches the blue in the cells of the rest harrow, a wild bean. In many insects something more happens to the pigments in the chemical lab of their bodies, and they come to the surface in a paint box of colors not found in their foods. When that laboratory is understood, perhaps then the pine sawyer beetle, the dead-leaf butterfly, and the bird-dropping moth will reveal their secrets of camouflage to man.

In the high ridges and summits of New Guinea where mosses flourish, two entomologists from the Bishop Museum, Honolulu, Hawaii, have discovered an extraordinary beetle, a large leaf-eating weevil that carries small gardens on its back that match its surroundings. The plants are fungi, algae, lichens, liverworts, and moss. The gardens are so real that living among the plants are animals, mites, rotifers, and minute nematodes. Approximately nineteen different species of plants have been found on these inch-long beetles that have niches, pits, ridges and tubercles to protect and hold their garden plants, some of which reproduce on the weevils. J. L. Gressitt believes the gardens may be distasteful to predators as well as being a camouflage, for although they climb to the top shoots of plants at night and foggy weather, no evidence of predation was observed. One individual was found killed, possibly by a mammal, but the garden was not touched, only the belly of the weevil was eaten or removed, probably because it was inhabited by seventy-five individual mites.

Searchlights of eerie material and construction are used to drive off enemies and sometimes attract food by two species of light fish that live in the coral reefs off the Banda Islands of Indonesia. Luminescent bacteria are somehow collected in pouches under the fishes' eyes. The bacteria glow constantly, and in order to turn them off the incredible fish have devised switches. One fish brings a window shade up over its pouches to shut off the beam, while the other rotates the pouch into a pocket. When turned on the lights beam through the water like a flashlight.

Just why the squid lights up like Coney Island at night is not known, but the deep-sea varieties of this complex animal radiate several different colors through organs that have reflectors, lenses, and pigment screens. The black-hooded squid *Vampyroteuthis infernalis* has colored lights and spotlights, while a relative *Thaumatolampas diadema* has lights of a pearly luminescence along the side of the body. The center of the eyes shine brilliant blue. On the front of the belly are lights as red as rubies, while on the rear a single sky blue light gleams among clusters of white ones for reasons no man knows. Defense, protection, courtship, food getting—all four and none are the best guesses of the scientists who have seen

*The baby ventriloquist*

and pondered the reasons for these exquisite light shows of the sea.

Confusion seems to be the protective trick of the nestling red-breasted grosbeak, one of which I raised when a child brought it to me after finding it on the ground following a thunderstorm. I decided to keep it until it could fly and placed it on a perch by the kitchen sink where I could hear it when it called in hunger. So clear and piercing was its voice that I realized I would be able to hear it outside my study, so I put it on a twig in the forsythia bush by the door where it was more at ease. About twenty minutes later I did hear it call and went out to feed it, only to hear it in the rhododendron bush. I was surprised that it had moved, for its wings were by no means well-developed. I went to that bush to feed it. It then called from the hedge. I went there. It called from the rhododendron. Thoroughly mystified, I walked back to the door, pushed the forsythia leaves apart, and saw, as I was beginning to suspect, that the nestling was perched where I had placed it. The little bird was a ventriloquist!

Fortunately for both me and the bird, the resident grosbeaks responded to its cries and the next morning were feeding it with no confusion at all. The little bird would call from the hedge, and the adults would fly to the forsythia and stuff it with food.

Another trick of birds is injury feinting, an act that never fails to fill me with wonder. I always watch a bird that has never had an injury or for that matter probably never seen another bird with a broken wing put on a demonstration. The killdeer is the most convincing of these actors for it stumbles, lists, and cries as it lures predators away from its nest and young.

When the home of this bird is approached, the female will run a few steps, drop her wing to the ground, and drag it pathetically. Upon seeing this, fox, weasel, or man, the predator's reaction is the same—catch the crippled bird. They pursue it. When followed, the bird runs ahead a few steps, falls to the ground, leans to one side, and flaps her "broken wing" while crying in alarm. As the predator sneaks closer to her, she recovers, runs a few feet and repeats the performance again. The first time I saw this, even though I had heard about injury feinting, I was so convinced that the killdeer had a broken wing that I followed her from the field where her nest lay into a marsh before she flew off and left me knee-deep in mire.

The American turkey, the common loon, and the Wilson's plover feint courtship instead of an injury. This is very conspicuous behavior that attracts attention, as proved by the numerous kills during the breeding season. So convincing is this act that one Wilson's plover left her nest at the approach of an ornithologist, spun into her courtship dance, and was mounted by her mate, who was inspired to copulate with her.

Faked broken wings and courtship, as ingenious as they are, at least are bird-like and, in that sense, understandable. But the female green-tailed towhee can imitate a mammal. If a hawk swings low over her nest, she will drop straight to the ground like an animal that has lost its footing, then throw up her tail and scurry away in a perfect imitation of a chipmunk, complete to bounces and darts. This act must, if nothing else, confuse a hawk who has been concentrating on the movements of a bird, not a mammal.

The white-sided jack rabbit of the Southwest, on the other hand, imitates the shifting mirages of its desert home, a trick that requires a muscle control exhibited by no other mammal. It sits as long as possible, somehow knowing that to most of its enemies moving is seeing. When about to be stepped upon, it throws up the hairs of its body and explodes from its cover like a burst of wild sunlight. This invariably startles the predator, he hesitates, and the rabbit proceeds to flash white, then dark, appearing and disappearing into the distance. He does this by shifting the white fur of the belly up to one side then the other and the dark fur of his side down to his belly, a slipping of skin that exceeds even the horse. As white changes to dark, then dark to white, the animal shimmers like a mirage as he dodges one way then another across the desert floor. He finishes his act by suddenly lowering his ears and stopping abruptly. The eye of the observer travels on in the direction of the fleeing animal, and the rabbit is lost from sight.

Playing dead is the remarkable deceit of the American opossum, a bit of theater that not only simulates a dead opossum, but one that has died in violence. When cornered, the opossum suddenly falls limply on one side and partially closes its eyes and achieves that glassy stare of death. If approached, its tongue buckles and hangs from its mouth. And when picked up and turned over, its legs fall limp, its body flops. The animal looks for all the world as if it had been strangled.

Frankly, I have never understood who the opossum thinks he is fooling except perhaps a man, who might, upon cornering one of these animals and seeing it drop dead, stuff it into his hunting jacket, only to have it awaken and take off at the first chance. A dead opossum to a fox or vulture, it seems to me, is asking to be eaten, but the act persists and the opossums have not only increased in numbers but spread northward into Canada. His success indicates that whatever the opossum is doing it is right for the opossum.

All these acts, however, are but short stage skits compared to the flounder whose entire life is one great bluff. Not only does it change color to match light sands, dark rocks, mottled gravel beds, but when brought into a lab and put on blue, bright green, or purple backgrounds—colors it would never come upon at sea bottom—this fish turns blue, bright green, and purple. Furthermore, its entire appearance is a lie.

When a flounder hatches from its egg, it is a perfectly normal fish with eyes on either side of its head, a back that faces upward, and a belly that is down. For two weeks it, like a minnow or a goldfish, swims freely from the bottom to the surface of the water. At this date, however, a drastic change begins. The flounder slowly sinks to the bottom, listing as it goes, until it can no longer right itself and is lying on its side, one eye looking up, the other in the mud, a position that puts it at a distinct disadvantage when foraging. To correct this, the eye that looks down into the sand gradually shifts to join the other, either by actually sliding up over the head, as some scientists state, or, more likely, by remaining where it is while the skull develops outward from the cheek to bring both eyes on top. To me either system is incredible.

Meanwhile, the belly and back are adjusting to the bottom of the sea. They grow outward across the floor to create that platter that is the flounder, a fish that lies on its side while imitating a fish that is on its belly. To complete the illusion of a normal fish, the side of the flounder that is up takes on the dark coloring characteristic of a fish back, and the side that is down grows light like a belly. At the age of six to twelve weeks, at the size of approximately an inch, the flounder has completed one of the greatest pieces of theater on earth.

Smallness is the protection of the candiru, a fish of the fresh waters of Brazil so infinitesimally tiny that it lives in the gills of larger fish. When the host fish breathes out, the candiru heads up this stream that leads into the gills. Here the tiny fish throws up its spines to keep from being ejected as the water flows out. In this extraordinary fish bowl, the chamber that surrounds the gills, it swims and eats the microorganisms in the water and settles to the bottom of the cavity to rest and sleep.

Tiny as it is, the candiru is a terrifying creature to the natives of Brazil, for it can enter the penis of a man, and once in, cannot be eliminated. The sharp backward-pointing spines hold it in place piercing the tissue painfully when the man eliminates. Should it reach the bladder, it kills the man. Only an excruciating operation before the victim reaches a hospital and while the fish is still in the urethra can prevent a man's death from this minuscule beast.

The waters of the world teem with chemists that defend themselves with venom. Sting rays, elephant fish, surgeonfish (a blade edged with poison shoots out near the tail), rabbitfish, dragonets, star gazers, sea snakes, all have appendages that sting. Among the invertebrate stingers, various jellyfish, shellfish, octopi, bristle worms, and sea urchins strike with weapons that are infused with chemicals similar to the stinger of the bee. A few of these chemicals are so severe that they can cause respiratory difficulties, paralysis, delirium, convulsions, and death in man.

Perhaps because of the bee and wasp, sea animals that sting

do not seem unique, but the electric animals—the catfishes, star gazers, electric eels, and rays—have astounded man since the ancients discovered their shock effects. Two of these, the electric eels and rays, can deliver a charge of anywhere from 8 to 220 volts, enough to knock a man down or light an electric light bulb. How? I always ask, for I don't even understand the current that comes into my house.

The electric organs of the rays comprise about one-sixth of the total body and are situated on either side of the anterior part of the pectoral fin near the head. They extend from about the level of the eye backward past the gill region and are composed of columnar prism-like structures separated by loose connective tissue, forming a network like honeycomb. The wonder is: the belly side of the ray is electrically negative, the back side positive. This seems so preposterous it escapes me.

No one knows just how the electric shock is produced, but it is believed to be a simple reflex action. When the eel is touched, the animal somehow reacts, the water completes the circuit, and enemies are knocked unconscious.

When I told my son about the electric eel, he was delighted and challenged me to find a creature that could out-do this one. I found several.

Along the coasts of every continent in muddy flats that are covered by the tide, lives the sea cucumber, a holothurian related to the starfish. As its name implies, it is long and slender like a garden cucumber and around its mouth at one end is a circle of fleshy tenacles that whirl and suck the microorganisms in the muddy waters into the body of this lethargic animal. The sea cucumber can move, but rarely does, preferring, if possible, to spend its life where it was born. When, however, it is attacked, this hopeless animal defends itself by ejecting all its innards! In a supreme effort to escape, it shoots at its enemy a murky cloud of breathing organs, digestive tract, gonads, tentacles, pharynx, intestines—almost every gut and viscera its owns—then collapses like a stuck balloon.

*The exploding sea cucumber*

Crabs and fish become entangled and die in the mess, some of which is poisonous, but the gutless sea cucumber usually lives on. Within its body still lie those marvelous regenerative organs of its phylum Echinodermata, and these begin to restore the system. Six months to two years may pass before the innards are recreated and the incredible sea cucumber is back to normal. Most of the reconstruction is done without benefit of anything more than a mouth and the whirling tentacles that slosh sea water into the hollow and feed the growing parts.

The sea cucumber cannot be mentioned without referring to another animal that protects itself in an extraordinary way. The Fierasfer fish of the South American coastal waters takes up his home within the anus of the sea cucumber. Strange indeed is a fish that dwells in an alimentary canal, but even more strange, it chooses the canal of an animal which upon the slightest irritation, will eject it and even poison it. To overcome this, the Fierasfer has practically no irritating fins, just a soft ribbon-like structure down its back. It enters its home cautiously, moving backwards in the current as the cucumber eliminates. Once inside, the Fierasfer moves about as little as possible. Unlike most fish whose anal openings are near the tail, the Fierasfer's alimentary canal opens under the lower jaw, so that by merely poking its head out of the sea cucumber it can eliminate.

The Fierasfer has gone beyond all reason to defend itself, but the slime eel seems to have gone beyond the laws of physics. A primitive fish, *Myxine glutinosa,* it is known from the Arctic to Massachusetts and in deep water as far south as North Carolina. This blind, finless creature that is but a foot and a half long can throw off a hundred times more mucus than there is animal—over two gallons of it! The slime eel spends the daylight hours buried in the soft bottom mud. At night, with the barbels on its snout, it drills into the bodies of fish held captive on fishermen's lines or gill nets. In this food case men bring it to the surface where, grasped, it turns on its fountain of slime. Like the porridge mill of nursery tale fame, the eel manufactures so much mucus that it seems the beast itself would be drained to the size of a pencil. It is not, but alive and active in the mountain of repulsive matter

*Fierasfer fish entering its living home*

that it exudes from every pore and gland, the slime eel wriggles free of a man's grip, or is so repugnant to him that he tosses it back into the sea.

The eggs of this unusual fish are also well protected. They are covered with a hard tough shell and at each end arises a cacti garden of barbed filaments. With these, the big eggs stick in clusters to whatever they come in contact with, be it a rock or the mouth of a predacious fish.

Only mad men resort to the weapon of the larva of the Cassida beetle. This creature swings a bag of its own excrement at its enemies. The bag, black, lumpy, and repulsive-looking, is held over the back of the larva by a two-pronged fork that can maneuver it in virtually any direction. In the package are not only all the excrement the animal has ever passed, but the dried skins of its many molts. The chief enemy of this larva is the ant which approaches the tasty grub, and to test its delectability, first strokes it with its forelegs, then sniffs it with its antennae, then bites. With this, the great black package is flung between the ant and its meal. Possibly because the bag is inanimate, most ants lose interest in the Cassida. A few, however, have bitten into the bag in experiments run by Dr. Thomas Eisner of Cornell, who recently discovered that this "fecal shield" was actually a defense mechanism. The ants that took a bite recoiled and turned away. Those that dashed off, however, were the individuals that had been swatted with the part of the package that held the wet, fresh feces. In a few cases these ants were smeared with feces. They bolted off to clean their dirty appendages or drag their contaminated mouthparts against the ground as ants do when hit with chemical pesticides. Only twice in several dozen experiments did ants succeed in biting the larva before it could swing its shield between them, and of the two only one was fatally injured. For the most part, the Cassida larva defended itself, perhaps not with honor, but certainly with effectiveness.

So legendary is the mass suicide of the lemmings, a device to protect an entire species against overpopulation, that rumor and fantasy have surrounded the act for generations. Some people have said they turn and run into the sea, others that they eat themselves out of house and home and die of starvation. Not long ago scientists believed that when populations reached a peak some switch inside the females was pulled and they gave birth to but one or two young instead of six or seven. Although there are still guesses as to what triggers the death throes, it is now known what kills them—not the sea, not the food, but an agent in the bloodstream of the lemming.

Two researchers working separately, David A. Mullen of the University of San Francisco and William B. Quay of the University of California, have found a substance in lemming blood that acts like an "antifreeze." It enables the lemmings to be active in the cold hours of winter when no other small mammals can live without hibernating. The antifreeze keeps the blood flowing to all parts of the body and prevents it from freezing. Should a warm spell hit the Alaskan tundra around Point Barrow where the animals were studied, the antifreeze causes the blood to clot and kill. Although the two doctors hope to find out what this antifreeze is that men might use it when planes come down in the Arctic and people are subjected to below zero weather, they as yet know only that it exists. Its formula is still a mystery.

This much is known, the antifreeze does kill them, but whether or not the warm weather sets it off is still being argued. Some scientists believe that the condition of overpopulation itself produces a hormone that sets off the antifreeze. Its release drives them wild, they run like mad men over rocks, through streams, across the tundra, on, on until they drop dead. In Norway the terrain on which the lemmings dwell slopes downward to the sea cliffs and the frantic animals, taking the line of least resistance, follow the land contours and plunge to their death in the seas—hence the tale of the mass suicide of the lemmings.

Despite disagreements as to what triggers the flow of the antifreeze, scientists are getting close to solving the most dramatic population cycle of all living mammals.

Extraordinary in the art of self-defense is the bombadier beetle. Years ago my father introduced me to this handsome creature with the warning, "Don't pick it up! It blasts off a bomb that can burn you."

Recently chemists at Cornell University have analyzed this bomb that actually goes off with a hissing "pfttt," when the beetle is either picked up or attacked by the ants that are its primary enemy. And it is a real bomb, a boiling hot (212°F.) mixture of lethal chemicals.

The artillery consists of two glands that lie in the tip of the abdomen. Each gland has a reservoir and a vestibule; the reservoir is a crucible where the ammunition is mixed—solution of chemical substances fed by other secretory tissues to manufacture hydroquinones, a foul smelling substance of brownish color. To this is added hydrogen peroxide, an active oxidizing agent.

A valve is controlled by a muscle that lies between the reservoir and the vestible in which there are enzymes that come from cells lining the walls. The enzymes are the igniters or catalysts that instantly break down the hydrogen peroxide, a process that in turn forces the oxidation of the hydroquinones.

When it is threatened, the bombadier beetle prepares to fire by shooting some of the reservoir fluid into the enzyme-filled vestibule. The powerful chemical reaction takes place the moment the two substances meet. Free oxygen gushes from the reaction with a sudden build up of temperature and pressure. The activated mixture pops from the beetle's body and is shot far and accurately like a hot spray from an aerosol can.

Each beetle is able to shoot about twenty-nine bullets of hot quinone in quick succession before needing to rest and refuel.

These beautiful beetles are about a half an inch long and have a head and thorax of bright orange and wings of brilliant blue. They live all over the world in subtropical and tropical climates and run rapidly over the forest floor at night hunting for food. By day they rest under rocks and logs.

How this beetle can withstand the hot temperatures of its own explosion is now under study by Dr. Thomas Eisner and his colleagues. Their guess is that the bombadier has developed its chemical and heat-resistant chitin to perfection.

No other defense, I thought, could compare with the bombs of the bombadier, so I collected one and mounted it. This seemed to me the ultimate in animal wizardry. Hardly had I come to this conclusion than I discovered another fantastic soldier—a modern dragon that shoots blood from its eyes.

*The blood-squirting lizard*

In a sandy terrarium in my son's room, a western horned lizard was sluffing off his skin. An inhabitant of the region of Texas and Arizona, this familiar household pet (often called a horned "toad") is adorned with cactus-like spines on its head and a fringe of spikes down the sides of its abdomen. There are three species. Running with celerity over rocks and sands, they submerge in the soil to rest. The individual in my son's room had lain still for so many days after molting that, concerned for its health, I reached into the terrarium to pick it up. In a second the head seemed to swell, the corner of the eyes redden, and from that tiny dragon a squirt of blood shot forth in a stream that chilled my nerves. It was the first time I had ever seen this and though I knew about this blood shooting, I had no idea how terrifying it could be when it suddenly happens.

# INVENTIVE WAYS TO LIVE WITH MAN

LAST summer I found I was no longer adding to the categories in my files on unconventional zoology. There seemed to be no other direction to proceed.

On July 20, 1969, Astronauts Neil A. Armstrong and Edwin E. Aldrin stepped down on the moon and turned their TV cameras back on the earth. No man who viewed his planet that night was not somehow disturbed, for not a trace of our remarkable achievements could be seen. We were all down there in tall buildings, on broad highways, in sprawling metropolises, but only one thing showed—the glow of all life together.

For many this was a turning point in thinking. The earth is not ours. Humans are only a small part of a glorious interacting system that creates one beautiful light in the blackness of space and as such we are but one more environment for the experimenting millions of animals to adjust to, to live in.

The following morning I walked through the canyons of New York seeing man from the outside looking in. Cities, bridges, artifacts, wastes, even our scientific prying were one more ecosystem in which some beasts have found a niche and have established a new category of animal—those that interact with and use man's world. Among these are some of the most miraculous and durable. The black and brown rats, hunted and persecuted, have survived by understanding us better than we do, as they circumvent extinction by producing generations of offspring that are better and better adapted to us. Certainly the house fly, various insects, and even snakes have achieved one of the miracles of living with man—DDT-resistant strains. Another animal that has improved by knowing us is the American red fox, who, rather than succumb to our hunting pressures as the Eastern cougar and the plains wolf did, have sharpened its wits against the wits of man. The species went on to breed even cleverer red foxes that can trip traps with a stick and run the tops of fences to avoid leaving scent on the ground for hounds to follow.

Several qualifications may provide adjustment to the man environment: a sensitive and fast reproductive clock (the house fly), sharp wits (rats and foxes), or—charm. An animal with all three is the blue tit (*Parus caeruleus*) that lives in the environment of the nature-loving British. One of twelve species of European tits (birds related to our chickadees), the blue tit is about the size of a walnut, black-eyed, quick moving, and cute. Capped with blue feathers, it has a charming black face mask and bib, clean white cheek patches, and a warm yellow breast. Together the demureness and coloration evoke a protective attitude in man that inhibits his aggression and permits the tit to take over as nesting sites flower pots, rain spouts, sacks and jugs, something that would not be tolerated in, for instance, a mouse.

The blue tit eats a variety of foods: nuts, grains, insects, food scraps of man, a factor that makes the man environment a highly suitable niche for it. The variety of its diet, furthermore, has sharpened its curiosity, and it will investigate almost anything for new sources of food. It will strip bark from trees and limbs to find insects, pick up stones to uncover spiders and beetles, and crack open objects in a quest for possible nut meats. Finally it is a social bird, most of whom accept man more readily than do solitary animals. During the spring and summer tits live in family groups; in autumn they team up with other tits and resident birds, knowing innately that many pairs of eyes and ears find more food and detect enemies quicker than a single pair.

Given curiosity and a catholic taste for food, it was inevitable that the tit would eventually come into some kind of conflict with man, and so it did. Early one morning in 1921 a housewife of Swaythling, England, a small town south of London, stepped to her front door to bring in her milk and found that an inch or more of cream was gone. She carried the bottle to the kitchen, berating the neighbor's cat and child only to discover later in the day that her neighbor also had been robbed of cream. The two women decided the milkman had something to do with it and confronted him the following morning. He scratched his head and said that there had been other complaints in the neighborhood and suggested that it might be the birds that were doing it. Every morning he was met at the corner by seven or eight tits that followed him down the block as he delivered milk.

The housewives were up early the next morning and no sooner had the milkman deposited the bottles and departed than down from the trees came the blue tits. One gripped the rim of a bottle with its small feet and, beating its wings, whacked the lid with its beak. The cardboard stopper tilted, the bird pulled it out, carried it to a nearby bush and dropped it. He returned to sip cream—and the truth was out.

Several autumns later people in towns almost exactly ten miles away complained about cream robbery and were told by Swaythlingers that they too, had "cream tits." Good bird watchers, the townspeople speculated as to why a resident bird that lives out its life in an acre or two of land would travel ten miles to sip cream in another town.

Years passed and the habit spread to the delight of many Britishers until about 1940 when the amusing trick became a problem. Almost everyone in southern England was being robbed, as well as the people in Scotland, Ireland, and Wales, and most were not enchanted.

In an effort to quiet complaints, officers of the milk industry met in 1944 to put a quick end to cream sipping by shifting from waxed cardboard to metal stoppers and by instructing customers to put stones, pots, jelly lids, and towels out at night for the milkman to cover bottles with.

For several months after the new lids were installed and stones put in place, cream sipping declined and everyone thought they had foiled the birds. They did not, however, know that the tits had been stealing so long that they had learned new skills. One day a man in the suburbs reported to the newspaper that he had watched a blue tit remove a stone from his milk bottle three days in succession. "The bird sat on the stone," he wrote, "and pounded it until it jiggled forward and hung over the top of the bottle. Then the tit stood on the projecting edge, tumbled the stone to the sill, and flitted to the bottle rim." Within the month a woman near Ipswich wrote a London paper that she had left tea cloths out for the milkman to cover the bottles, had become irritated because he was not using them, and arose early one morning to complain. To her astonishment she saw her tea cloth rise into the air above the bottles, a blue tit jabbing it with feet and beak as he and his friends pulled it away and dropped it on the steps.

Stones and tea cloths removed, the metal lids were no problem at all to the tits. They "pierced, drilled, lifted, twisted or simply flipped them into the air," said reports in the magazine *British Birds*.

War weary, besieged by bombs and the constant threat of death, the British became joyously involved in observing the antics of the little birds. The British Broadcasting Company asked all citizens robbed of cream to get up a few minutes early and take notes on how the birds opened bottles. Dates, locations, and techniques were wanted by the British Trust for Ornithology for several reasons: one, to find out how the habit spread, another to determine if a tit-proof lid was possible.

Thousands of descriptions and facts came in from the suburbs and country. One tit poked its bill under the cap and sipped, another tore the metal into fine strips and tossed them away, while others simply drilled through the metal and drank. A few fell in and drowned. No one technique prevailed. The milk industry abandoned the project and the BBC announced that the best way to stave off the thieves was to put the milk in boxes. A few people did so only to find that, cut off at the box, the tits flew to the wagon and sipped cream while the milkman was delivering.

Other data from the citizenry proved more enlightening, and the British Trust for Ornithology published an account on how the habit spread. In the early spring before the breeding season, tit families break up and the young leave their parents' territories to settle down almost exactly ten miles from home. The young of the original cream sippers of Swaythling had learned from their parents by observing them and upon moving to a new homesite had apparently taught the birds there.

The British people adjusted to the birds by accepting their cream sipping and the fuss had about died down when another crisis arose. In 1949 from hedged cottage and woodsy suburb came complaints that strips, even sheets, of wallpaper were either missing from rooms or hanging in tatters. Bedroom curtains were reported in shreds, cakes of precious soap unwrapped and demolished as the tits invaded house and home.

When, however, a tit flew into a kitchen, tore the labels off two bottles, and a man drank paint thinner instead of ale, paper tearing became a problem. The BBC went on the air suggesting that people close their windows and once more take notes, this time on how, when, and where the birds tore paper.

Ornithologists at Oxford University analyzed these and reported that the tits did not eat the paper nor did they use it for nests, but were, once more, being ingenious about finding food. The autumn of 1949 had been dry, the food supply was short, and to overcome this the birds had investigated every possible new source of food in man's environment in the same way that they stripped bark from trees to find insects.

The explanation was clear enough but did not prevent an uproar at Haileybury College when a flock of twenty tits came in through the dome of the chapel, riddled the plaster with forty holes, and scattered debris from the altar to the belfry. They furthermore placed a student's career in jeopardy when they entered his room the day before exams and tore all the jackets off his books. He claimed he could no longer tell the Latin from the math book and was not responsible for his grades.

At the end of the drought the paper tearing ceased, but not the milk sipping. This still goes on in the British Isles today for a very British reason. When I asked Dr. Harry Champion, Dean of the Oxford Forestry School, how the matter could be solved, his eyes twinkled. "I guess we'll simply have to abandon the Isles," he said. "We can't change our habit of putting milk on our stoops and we can't harm the birds."

Although the blue tits' use of man's environment is beloved by the British, not every animal's is. The owner of a nut and bolt factory situated in a town near the coast in England decided to make life more pleasant for his employees by installing glass skylights. Near the factory was a dump where imperfect nuts and bolts were discarded until they could be smelted and re-used. Then the skylight was completed, the glass reflected the rays of the sun with such brilliance that flocks of curious herring gulls flew over the factory to investigate. To them no doubt it was one huge rock. Then when they saw the dump pile they reacted according to their instinct, descended, picked up the bolts and nuts and dropped them on the skylight. Result—one nearly destroyed factory and a morale-shattered working force.

As an environment we probably serve the cockroach better than any environment they have encountered in the 350 million years they have lived on this earth. Having survived fire and flood, glaciers, land upheavals, and volcanic action, having been pursued and devoured by animals, the cockroach finds the world of man a tropical isle. We provide for it shelter, moisture, warmth, and an abundance of food from the kitchen to the closet where ties and clothes with grease spots hang. Although there are about 3500 species of cockroaches, only about thirty-five have moved in with us, the others remaining in forests, plains, and deserts. But the thirty-five have settled down in every suitable niche including television sets. Here tubes keep them warm and paraffin feeds them.

Occasionally adult populations of cockroaches are set back by fumigants and pesticides, but their eggs are durable and many survive to hatch and bring forth stronger young. We seem only to improve this animal.

Since we provide a tricky environment that requires intelligence to survive, we tend to eliminate the stupid animals and sharpen the resourcefulness of the bright. The auk is gone, but the gulls and blackbirds are on the increase for many reasons. One is that we have created perfect resting and occasionally breeding areas for these birds when we built aircraft runways. By 1968, these habitats caused three fatal plane accidents and about a million dollars in damage to aircraft each year. The most serious accident occurred in 1960—an Electra taking off from the Boston airport crashed when starlings clogged the jet engines, killing sixty-two persons. Wildlife experts were called in and they attempted to scare the birds off the runways with blank cartridges, scarecrows, meteorological balloons, automatic acetylene guns, and tin pans beaten together. This was successful only until the starlings learned that the sounds would not harm them, and they returned to the wonderful runways that not only stayed warm long after dark but were often near dumps or harbors where garbage scows left cities daily laden with bird food.

When loud noises failed, the men turned to knowledge of bird behavior and made tapes of their alarm cries. These were played to the birds from loud speakers mounted along runways just before take-offs and landings. This too was successful, but briefly; the starlings soon learned that the sounds came from the boxes and ignored the calls. Many adapted so well they used the speakers for roosts.

In 1967 the Newark, New Jersey, Airport had a near-fatal accident, and in the light of new research the language of the birds was once more investigated as a possible deterrent. Dr. John Kadilec, who had been studying birds and airports, was called in by the Port of Authority of New York, for he believed he knew why the alarm signals had not worked in Boston. He had discovered that a "distress" signal, that scream a bird gives when a tail feather is yanked out, was more effective than an alarm cry, and it was necessary to keep the call moving around like a bird. Since each species had its own distress cry, Kadilec taped the specific distress signal of the Newark birds, which were gulls, mounted a speaker on the roof of a car, and played while he drove around.

The results was spectacular. Not only did the gulls promptly depart from the Newark runways, but those overhead could be herded like cattle away from the area. In a few months the "squawk box" had changed the flight patterns of the gulls on their way to the dumps, and within the year they no longer passed over the airport but set up new routes to their food supply. The mobile unit is now used only about once or twice a month, generally for young birds that have not learned that somewhere on the ground below is "death."

No one feels, however, that the battle is won. The Director of Operations has learned that the smarter the men, the smarter the birds also become. "We no sooner get ahead of them," he said, "than they figure us out. I watch them like a hawk because I know one of these days they'll figure out that mobile unit and we'll have to think harder."

New animal ideas, like the washing of grain in the macaque monkeys and the opening of bottles by the blue tit, are usually discovered by one smart individual animal from whom the others learn. One such genius however was lost to its species before any others could copy her technique, an American egret named Frances, that lived in a suburb of St. Petersburg, Florida. Bulldozed out of her home by a housing project, Frances adjusted to her disrupted environment by making her evictors pay. Every morning she would make the rounds of the neighborhood, tap on front doors, and was fed by enchanted housewives. If she got no reply at the front door, she would go around to the back and scream until someone came to feed her. She had not estimated her resourceful and devious environment, however, and it was within the year that Frances got food poisoning. The distress cry went out among the egrets and the suburbs of St. Petersburg were relinquished to man, a decision undoubtedly the wisest in the long run.

Another species of egret, the cattle egret, has been so successful in adapting to man that it not only migrated from Africa to South America without being noted, but it had established itself in Florida for thirteen years before being detected. From there, it moved all the way up the eastern seaboard to Massachusetts before being identified on April 23, 1952 by William Drury, a young ornithologist out of Harvard. The embarrassment to the ornithology world was enormous. How could a bird appear among so many bird watchers for so many years without being recognized? The answer is partially that man's reasoning often gets in his way. The cattle egret according to textbooks and field guides was an African bird, a very specialized creature that lived only in association with rhinos, elephants, water buffalo, feeding on the insects they stir up in the brush and grass. It never occurred to anyone this egret could be anywhere but in Africa with their companion beasts.

The egret was not brought over by men as the starling was, nor is it likely that it made the trip riding on ships, for it is an extremely shy and retiring bird. The only other possibility is that it flew. By taking off from Cape Verde the egrets could have traveled 1700 miles on storm and trade winds to the Guianas in South America. Moving at a cruising speed of twenty miles per hour, the voyagers could make the crossing in about fifty hours—a possibility that most ornithologists believe happened. This spectacular migration is just one of many. Since Drury's identification of the bird, it has been reported in Europe, Asia, Newfoundland, in fact in every country in the world except Australia. It is now pushing west to California.

No one can explain such a sudden expansion and success. This the experts do know, however. The tall white bird with its long neck and buff tufts on the crown, throat and mantle, is the bird of the industrial world. It has found a niche in the United States not following cattle, but the tractors. Furthermore, unlike the tits who sip cream and are not particularly helpful to man, this bird most decidedly is. A farmer I talked to in Florida likes to see the great white flocks descend upon his fields when he is cultivating, for they catch everything in sight—insects, mice, even rats. "They save me a lot of money," he aid, " 'cause they can do in one day what it would take me barrels of pesticides and weeks to do."

The cattle egret may truly turn out to be "our" bird. Like us, they can learn. In Africa they eat only insects and rodents, but here they are varying their menu. Mrs. Isabelle Krome of Homestead, Florida, who has lived most of her long life near the Everglades, gave me her view of the cattle egret's success. "On several occasions," she said, "I've watched the

*Cattle egrets, far from home*

cattle egrets in the National Park walk with the American and snowy, the fishermen egrets. The cattle egrets eye them intently as they spear and eat fish, and one I saw cocked its head when a snowy caught a fish, then walked into the water and tried to fish, too. They'll get along," she added. "They can adapt to our mass agriculture, our machines, and the fish of our polluted waters."

Just as many birds have made use of the man environment, so have several mammals. The western deer mouse has extended its range since highways and bridges have linked together areas once geologically isolated. From their point of view, these attractive mice have three thousand more square miles of grassland prairie—the roadsides. Along the natural habitat of the gigantic pathways, the little fellow has moved east, crossing mountains and the Mississippi on new frontiers provided by man.

The coyote, along with the mouse, has trotted the highway

sides at night, fur swinging, belly filled with western deer mice, woodchucks, pheasants, voles, and other inhabitants of the roadside grasslands. Of course, no individual travels the distance alone, but rather along the way roadside dens were dug and the young were born. Like the blue tits, they move out of their parents' home—and on down the highway. The coyote has now reached the Adirondack Mountains in New York and the eastern edge of the Catskills.

As the coyote and mouse expand their ranges in the man-changed landscape, others cling to their homesteads with unbelievable tenacity. In December of 1964 such an individual arrived at the Humbolt County Fish Hatchery in Eureka, California. It was a coho salmon, *Oncorhynchus kisutch*. This fourteen-inch male had passed seemingly impossible obstacles erected by man to return to his spawning grounds. One of more than 25,000 salmon that were dumped into coastal streams by the State Game Commission, the young fish went out into the ocean off California in 1962.

Two years later, silver and full-grown, he was ready to spawn. His internal compass set, he headed landward and swam from the ocean into Redwood Creek. He then returned into Prairie Creek and passed the spot where he had been set free. A mile or so upstream he entered a drainage ditch. Fighting his way through culverts and past many tributary ditches, he entered a narrow slough and faced a four-inch pipe. Undeterred, he plunged into the pipe, took a right angle turn and swam upwards. A tight screen covered the exit. The salmon knocked the screen off and swam on only to be confronted by what the fisheries men described as an "impassable net." Bursting through this, he arrived with a swirl in the same tank in which he had been spawned, and that was it— he was home.

Although the coho, once a threatened species, is now being propagated and successfully returned to the seas, Americans have sent forty-six species of wildlife into extinction by either

altering the landscape or hunting. We did think we were
doing one thing right—trying to prevent forest fires. Twenty
years ago we learned almost too late that this can also be a
mistake. After World War II the Kirkland's warbler was
down to but a few pairs. No one knew why. A gray-black bird
with yellow breast and spotted sides, it wags its tail, sings
much like the trilling water thrush, and is singular because it
lives in two of the smallest areas of any bird. One is the jack
pine plants of central Michigan, an area sixty by one hundred
miles. The other is a few small islands in the Bahamas where
it winters. This unusual bird is found nowhere else in the
world.

Concern for its survival in the 1940s provoked ornithologists from the University of Michigan and the Audubon
Society to donate long hours to the study of the life history of
the bird. All hoped that some clue to its decline might be
found. Indeed it was.

The bird, they observed, would nest only in areas where
the trees (and they had to be jack pines) were between five
and eighteen feet tall. If the pines were any older or younger,
the warblers could or would not nest. A few raised offspring
in plantations where the trees were the correct size, but the
majority preferred clumps of jack pines beneath which grew
wintergreen, blueberry, sheep laurel, and sweet fern, an aro-
matic setting to which they were so specifically adapted they
could live nowhere else. Protected from the lightning fires
that had adjusted their nesting grounds for unknown ages,
the birds, under man's kind rules, had been deprived of nesting sites.

Today the scene in the jack pine barrens is horrifying to
many tourists as they witness men lighting forest fires or
chopping down trees. When they complain, they are told the
birds approve. Apparently they do, for their population is
steadily increasing as enlightened men realize that preserving
our wildlife is more complicated than just protecting it.

No people are more aware of this than the staff of the government's newest and most popular bureau, the Endangered Wildlife Research Program of the Department of Interior. This outfit is devoted to capturing threatened species and propagating them for release to the wilds. The program came into existence in the fall of 1965, and one of the first assignments was to save the masked bobwhite quail from extinction. In 1966 Senator Karl Mundt of South Dakota urged the bureau to obtain a few captive birds from a ranch in Tucson and to restore them to Arizona. Before the great cattle drives destroyed the grasses of the southwest in the 1800s, the masked bobwhites were a common bird of the desert. Today at the most twenty-seven are alive in the back country of Mexico, according to the owner of the land.

Five eggs arrived at Patuxent, Maryland, where the Research Program has its laboratory and headquarters. Shortly after hatching, two of the rare chicks drowned in a shallow dish of water. This seemed unreasonable until one of the ecologists recalled that he had never seen open water in the desert where the quails lived. Pebbles were put in the dish and the other three chicks did not drown, but refused to eat. Ray Erickson, director, took the babies home and spent most of the night on his knees trying to teach them to eat. They refused. At dawn one of his staff members called him to say he had a last desperate thought. He reminded Erickson that all species of quail grow up in coveys and wondered if they needed to have more company. Erickson put the three chicks in a covey of young quail, and they tipped their heads, eyed the other little ones pecking, and immediately began to perk up and feed.

The endangered wildlife staff has shown that ecology is more complicated than they had ever anticipated. Not only were plants and stones important, but interpersonal relations.

For lack of knowledge or the lack of inherited intelligence

of the animals, the balance of nature once upset is difficult to re-establish.

Along the stream banks of England, competing with the fishermen for fish and the bird lovers for birds, one of the most valuable animals to man has become a pest—the mink. A thousand are trapped every year by the Ministry of Agriculture's Infestation Control Laboratory. They are the offspring of those that escaped from fur farms and set up housekeeping in Britain's glorious countryside.

More damaging than they, according to the Ministry, are the coypu (also called nutria), a native rodent of South America that resembles a beaver except for the tail—the coypu has none. It took to the countryside when its fur lost popularity and the coypu ranchers set them free. With sugar beets and other crops to sustain them, they have multiplied so rapidly that 136,000 were killed between 1965 and 1968—to no avail. The coypu breeds on and may soon, like the English or house sparrow in this country, become an accepted member of the human community of Great Britain. After a century of berating the English sparrow, the American Ornithologists' Union gave up the battle and placed this bird on the official list of American birds in 1967. In addition to its scientific name, *Passer domesticus domesticus*, they gave it its worldwide common name, the house sparrow. It was finally described in U.S. scientific journals as a bird that is widely distributed in cities, towns, and farms throughout the United States and Canada.

Of all the beasts that have adapted to us, none is more terrifying than the cryptic moth, *Phigalia titea*. Before 1915 the moth was known in common language as the peppered moth, for it was white with pale specks in its wings.

That year in the industrial centers of New Jersey a black phase appeared that matched the soot on trees, fences, and buildings. Entomologists referred to it as "the industrial

*Adjusting to pollution*

moth." In 1940 this black phase began a population explosion and turned up in all the dirty industrial areas of the northeast, the first creature to adjust to the color of pollution. The blackness is now inherited.

In 1968 T. D. Sargent of the University of Massachusetts at Amherst collected the black phase in the beautiful town of Leverett, far removed from industrial pollution. When he released them he found that they rested on white oaks and other light trees where they were highly conspicuous. Wrote the entomologist: "In such circumstances, strong selection pressure for a more appropriate background might be expected."

Perhaps in Leverett the industrial moth may seek out chimneys or dark lampposts. On the other hand, it may need only to wait for the blackened environment to come to it. Do they anticipate? No scientist will answer this.

Even the things that we do right are not necessarily the result of our thinking, but accident. In 1968 unbeknownst to man at the time, the felt-tipped markers became one of the most dramatic possibilities for insect control. At the Department of Agriculture's Entomological Research Center, Tifton, Georgia, three scientists, Richard L. Jones, Robert L. Burton, and Malcolm C. Bowman were running experiments on the corn earworm moth. Great numbers of the larva were raised, and in the course of collecting them the entomologists marked the cloth on which the insects deposited their eggs with felt-tipped marking pens. After a few days had passed the scientists noticed that more eggs were laid near the ink markings than anywhere else. They contacted the manufacturers of two brands and obtained a list of active ingredients in the markers they had been using, and finally isolated the chemical that made the moths lay. Tricetin and related compounds proved to be the magic chemical that induced the moths to lay. The three entomologists are now engaged in placing tricetin traps around cornfields in the hopes of luring the creatures with felt-tipped pens and controlling their outbreaks with well-placed lures less dangerous than insecticides. The eggs laid on cloth, the farmer of the future could pick them up in the morning and burn them in an incinerator.

As discouraging as our relationship with the earth's plants and animals may seem, there is one hope. We, too, have within us a slow time clock that senses the needs of the race and reacts. These clocks, like those in the industrial moth and the sparrow and all other animals, are set by the wind, the force of gravity, the temperature, and our numbers. Despite brains, our animal protoplasm is working for us to one purpose—the survival of the human race.

Thus we are the oddest of all the beasts. Possessed with the power to reason, gifted with the unconscious intelligence of living tissue, we as a species must go through the most elaborate gestures in the entire animal kingdom to behave normally.

Perhaps some day we will have figured out everything the animals know, and our minds will tell our bodies to carry the baby through feedings and sleep, to recoil from the presence of strontium-90, to drive away pests by using their own chemicals and signals, to keep the sea and land clean. At that time our intelligence will match the instincts of the lower forms of life and we will not have to drive wild things into extinction or rationalize our social disasters.

Yesterday I picked up a piece of lined school paper that had blown to the floor when I opened the porch door to spring. In the handwriting of my thirteen-year-old, Luke, scrawled under the title: "An Exciting Event that Happened to Me" were these words only:

"Monday was a bore, just like every day when you've been doing what you've been doing. Then our friend invited me to an American Association for the Advancement of Science Conference. She let me look through an electron microscope. . . ."

What will Luke collect?

# PRINCIPAL BIBLIOGRAPHY

Allen, Arthur A. *Book of Bird Life.* D. Van Nostrand Co., Inc., 1951.

Anderson, Sydney, and Jones, Knox J. *Recent Mammals of the World.* The Roland Press Co., 1967.

Austin, Oliver L., Jr. *Birds of the World.* Golden Press, 1961.

Allen, Glover Morrill. *Birds and Their Attributes.* Dover Publications, Inc., 1962.

Bardach, John. *Downstream.* Harper and Row, 1964.

Barnes, Robert D. *Invertebrate Zoology.* W. B. Saunders Co., 1963.

Breder, Charles M., Jr. *Marine Fishes of the Atlantic Coast.* G. P. Putnam and Sons, 1948.

Berger, Andrew J. *Bird Study.* John Wiley and Sons, Inc., 1961.

Coker, R. E. *This Great and Wide Sea.* Harper and Brothers, 1962.

Craighead, F. C., Sr. *Insect Enemies of Eastern Forests.* U. S. Department of Agriculture, Miscellaneous Publication No. 657, 1950.

Craighead, Frank C., and Craighead, John J. *Hawks, Owls and Wildlife.* Wildlife Institute, 1953.

Dorst, Jean. *The Migrations of Birds.* Houghton Mifflin Co., 1962.

Eisenberg, J. F. *The Tenrecs.* Smithsonian Contributions to Zoology, Number 27, 1970.

Elton, Charles. *Animal Ecology.* Sidgwick and Jackson, Ltd., 1927-1962.

Frost, S. W. *Insect Life.* Dover Publications, 1959.

Gertsch, Willis J. *American Spiders.* D. Van Nostrand Co., Inc., 1949.

Hamilton, W. J., Jr. *American Mammals.* McGraw-Hill Book Co., Inc., 1939.

Jameson, William. *The Wandering Albatross.* William Morrow and Co., 1959.

Jewel, P. A., and Loizos, Caroline. *Play, Exploration and Territory in Mammals.* Zoological Society of London, Academic Press, 1966.

Murie, Olaus J. *Field Guide to Animal Tracks.* Houghton Mifflin Co., 1954.

Nice, Margaret Norse. *Studies in the Life History of the Song Sparrow,* Vols. I and II. Transactions of the Linnaean Society of New York, 1937.

Olin, George. *Mammals of the Southwest Deserts.* Southwestern Monuments Association, 1954.

Palmer, Ralph S. *The Mammal Guide.* Doubleday and Company, Inc., 1954.

Pettingill, Olin Sewall, Jr., and Lancaster, Douglas A., Editors. *The Living Bird.* Seventh Annual, The Laboratory of Ornithology, Cornell University, 1968.

Pope, Clifford H. *Snakes Alive and How They Live.* Viking Press, 1962.

Rue, Leonard Lee, III. *The World of the Beaver.* J. B. Lippincott, 1964.

Russell, F. S., and Yonge, C. M. *The Seas.* Frederick Warner and Co., Ltd., 1960.

Schiller, Claire H., Editor. *Instinctive Behavior.* International Universities Press, Inc., 1957.

Scott, John Paul. *Animal Behavior.* University of Chicago Press, 1958.

Smith, Frank A., Pitelka, Donald P. Abbott, and Weesner, Frances M. *Intertidal Invertebrates of the Central California Coast.* University of California Press, 1964.

U. S. Department of Agriculture. *Insects, the Yearbook of Agriculture.* U. S. Government Printing Office, 1952.

Van Tyne, Josselyn, and Berger, Andrew J. *Fundamentals of Ornithology.* John Wiley and Sons, Inc., 1961.

Young, J. Z. *The Life of Mammals.* Oxford at the Clarendon Press, 1963.

*Journals*

*National Geographic Magazine*
*Nature, International Journal of Science*
*Science, American Association for the Advancement of Science*
*Scientific American*
*Wilson Bulletin*

Through the years I have, of course, used countless research sources, verified at later dates by current studies.

aardvark, 123
Akron, Ohio, University of, 11
*Agapornis* (African parrot), 84–85, *illus.*, 85
Agriculture, Department of, Entomological Research Center, Tifton, Georgia, 207
albatross, 39–41, 81
Alberta, Edmonton, University of, Zoology Lab, 9
Aldrin, Edwin E., 191
alligator, American, 101–103
American Association for the Advancement of Science, 208
American Museum of Natural History, New York, 15; Hall of Fishes, 63
American Ornithologists' Union, 205
American Society of Mammalogists, 64–65
amoeba, 49–50
anaconda snake, 64
*Anas acuta* (pintail duck of North America), 73
angler fish, 62–64, *illus.*, 63
anteater, 70, 123–124; spiny (echidna), 116, 124
*Antheraea* (silk moth), 79
ant lion, 127
aphid, 51, 164–165
aphid lion, 126–127
Apollo 12, 47
Archeozoic, 6
archer fish, 133
Argonne National Laboratory, Argonne, Illinois, 157
armadillo, 113–114, *illus.*, 113, 123
Armstrong, Neil A., 191
Atomic Energy Commission, 158
Audubon Society, 203
auk, 197

backswimmer, 32–33, *illus.*, 32
bacteria, 47, 49
Bailey, Vernon, 103–104
banded burrowing snake, 36
bandicoot, 64–65

barnacle, 10–11
bat, 70–72, 144, 153–154; of Panama (*Uroderma bilobatum*), 88
baya bird, 86
bear, 70; black, 115; grizzly, 115, 171–173
beaver, 90–93
bee, honey, 25–26, 60, 144–147, *illus.*, 145, 164, 182
beetle, bombadier, 188–189; Cassida, 186–187; click or elater, 30; pine sawyer, 174–175; whirligig (*Gyrinidae*), 165–166, *illus.*, 166
Bell's vireo, 112–113
Belostomatidae (water bug), 125–126, *illus.*, 126
biotelemetry, 172
bird, 37–42, 60, 64–69, 150–152, 166–169, see also under individual name
bird of paradise (Wallace's standard-wing), 69
bittern, 19
Bishop Museum, Honolulu, 176
blackbird, 169, 197; redwinged, 66
black snake, 37
blue racer snake, 37
boa, 36–37, 64; Cuban, 152–153
bowerbird, 67–69; golden, 67–68; regent, 68–69, *illus.*, 68; Sanford's golden-crested, 67
Bowman, Malcolm, 207
bristle worm, 182
British Museum, 74
British Trust for Ornithology, 195
brook stickleback, 99–101, *illus.*, 101
Bronx Zoo, New York, 163
Bullen, Frank T., 40
bunting, painted, 113
black skimmer, 86, 124
Burton, Robert L., 207
butterfly, 147, 176; Kallima, 175; sipping, 125

caddisfly, 77–78, *illus.*, 78
California Academy of Science, San Francisco, 46
California, University of, 156, 187

camel, 48
candiru, 182
cardinal, 112–113
Carpenter, Dr. C. R., 72
cat, 72, 115
catfish, 144, 161–163, *illus.*, 162, 183; gaff-topsail, 98–99, *illus.*, 98; walking, 43–44; yellow, 99
caterpillar, 175; leafroller, 78–79; leaf tyer, 79
*Cercaria I* (larval stage of fluke), 47
cerithium mollusks, 124
Champion, Dr. Harry, 196
Cheke, A. S., 73–74
chimpanzee, of Gombe Game Preserve, Africa, 137–138
Chinese pangolin, 123
chipmunk, 88–89
Ciliata, 49–50
*Cinclus mexicanus,* water ouzel of American Rockies, 93–96
clam, 24, 32
clingfish, 8
*Cnemidophorus,* 51
coach whip snake, 37
Coelenterate, 50
cockroach, 197
Colorado, University of, Museum, 51
Convoluta, 121–123
coot, 66
copperhead snake, 101, 152
coral, 24, 50; brain, 24
cormorant, 134
Cornell University, 186, 188
Cornell University's Ornithological Laboratory, 106
cougar, 192
cowbird, 109
coyote, 201–202
coyput (nutria), 205
crab, hermit, 9–10, *illus.*, 10
Craighead, Dr. Frank, 4, 172–173
Craighead, Dr. John, 4, 172
Craighead, Dr. F. C., Sr., 4
crossbill, red winged, 124; white winged, 124
crow, 151–132; fish, 136
cuckoo, 110; yellow-billed, 110
*Cynea artica* (largest jellyfish), 22

*Cyrinidae* (whirligig beetle), 165–166, *illus.*, 166

damsel fly, nymph of, 33
DDT, 48
deer, 144, 163
Desert Museum, 58
*Diademichthys lineatus,* 8
dog, 70, 115, 148–149, 163
dolphin, 44–46; blind *(susu),* 45
doodlebug, 128–129, *illus.*, 128
dragonet, 182
dragonfly, 33
dragonfly nymph, 33–34
Drury, William, 199–200
duck, farm, 108–109; black-headed, 109; pintail of North America *(Anas acuta),* 73
duck-billed platypus, 72, 117

eagle, 84; Florida bald, 84
echidna (spiny anteater), 116
*Echidnophaga gallinacea* (stickflea), 130
*Echinoderm* (sanddollar, starfish, sea urchin), 30–31
Ecole Polytechnique, Paris, 39
eel, 160; American, 61–62; electric, 183; European, 61–62; slime *(Maxine glutinosa),* 185–186
egret, 199; American, 201; cattle, 199–201, *illus.*, 201; snowy, 201
Eisner, Dr. Thomas, 186, 189
electric-light bug, 129–130
elephant fish, 182
*Elophila fulicalis* (moth), 33
Endangered Wildlife Research Program of the Department of Interior, 204
*Ephermerida* (Mayfly), 75
Erickson, Ray, 204
*Escherichia coli,* 9
Everglades National Park, 102, 114
Exobiology, 5

fairy shrimp, 141–142
Feder, H. M., 130
*Fenusa ulmi* (leaf miner), 2–4, *illus.*, 2
Fierasfer fish, 184–185, *illus.*, 185

finch, 125; Australian zebra, 66; Darwin's of Galapagos, 134–135, *illus.*, 135; woodpecker, 135–136
fish, 160–163
flamingo, 124–125
flatworm, 53
Florida Everglades, 103
Florida Fish and Game Commission, 44
flounder, 181–182
fluke (*Schistosoma mansohi*), 46–47; larval stage (*Cercaria I*), 47; parasitic, 53
fly, house, 192; stable, 164; tsetse of Africa, 164
flycatcher, 125; great crested, 169
flying fish, Atlantic, 147–148
fox, 70; flying, 71; red, 192
frigatebird, 18, 66–67
frog, red flying of Sumatra, 163–164

garfish, 103
garter snake, 64, 101
Georgia, University of, 72
Gertsch, Willis J., 132
gibbon, 72–73
goat, 163
goldfish, 160
goose, barnacle, 107; Canadian, 73; Chinese, 73
Graber, Robert, 112–113
Gressitt, J. L., 177
Griffin, Donald R., 153
grosbeak, 169; red-breasted, 178–179, *illus.*, 178
grunion, 80
gull, 197–199; herring, 110–112, *illus.*, 196–197; sea, 136

Haileybury College, 196
hawk, 19, 125, 144
hedgehog, 72
heron, 19; night, 66
*The Herring Gull's World*, 112
H.M.S. *Ark Royal*, 39
Hopcraft, John B. D., 106–107
Humbolt County Fish Hatchery, Eureka, California, 202
hornbill, 81, 104–105, *illus.*, 105

hummingbird, 40–42, *illus.*, 40, 84; bee, 41; ruby-throated, 41–42; South American, 42
hump-back whale, 11–12
hydra, 27–30, *illus.*, 28, 50
hydromedusa, 9

Idrac, Professor P., 39
iguana, 134
Indo-Pacific sea urchin, 8
insects, 60; see also under individual names
Institute of Marine Sciences, Miami, 97, 123

jacana, 43, 106–107
Jahn, Walter, 8
Jameson, Admiral William, 39
jellyfish, 22, 50, 182; largest (*Cynea artica*), 22; umbrella, 22
Jenkins, Dr. Dale, 5
Jet Propulsion Laboratory, Pasadena, 7
Johnsgard, Paul, 107
Jones, Richard, L., 207

Kadilec, Dr. John, 198
Kafatos, Dr. of Harvard, 79
Kalmbach, E. R., 151
kangaroo, 64–65, 70; gray, 114
Kawamura, S., 138
Kear, Janet, 107
Kelly, Dr. Roger, 11
Kent, England, University of, Chemical Laboratory, 9
Kety Committee, 6
killdeer, 179
King, Wayne, 163
kite, swallow-tailed, 140–141
kiwi, 156–157, *illus.*, 157
Kleiman, Devra, 148
Kramer, Gustav, 169
Krome, Mrs. Isabelle, 200–201
krill, 77

Lack, David, 150
Langley Research Center, Hampton, Virginia, 7
Laskey, Amelia, 86

Lawich-Goodall, Baroness Jane and Baron Hugo, 139
leaf miner (*Fenusa ulmi*), 2–4, *illus.*, 2
lemming, 187–188
Lerner Marine Laboratory, Bimini, 21
light fish, 177
lion, 118–120, 163
lizard, western horned (horned "toad"), 189–190, *illus.*, 189; whiptail, 50–51, *illus.*, 50
lobster, 158–159
locust, migratory, 169–171, *illus.*, 170; desert, 171
London, University of, 176; King's College, 154
London Zoological Society, 148
loon, 179
Lorenz, Konrad, 150

macromolecules, 7
magapode (mound builder), 84
*Mammalogy, Journal of*, 4
Maslin, Dr, Paul, 51
Massachusetts, University of, 206
Mayfly (*Ephermerida*), 75
medusa, 50
*Medusa of Eucopium*, *illus.*, 23
"metabolism detector," 7
Michigan, University of, 4, 27, 65, 203
Microtus (field mouse), 103–104
Ministry of Agriculture in Surrey, England, 12
Ministry of Agriculture's Infestation Control Laboratory, England, 205
mink, 205
minnow, 161
mole, 144
mollusk, 20–21, 24
mouse, 71, 115; deer, 71, 201; field (Microtus), 87, 103–104, pine, 115, Shaw's jird, 71
monkey, howling, 72; long-tailed macaque of Singapore Botanical Garden, 138; macaque of Japan, 138; rhesus, 72; South American Capuchin in London Zoo, 138–139; spider, 70
Morris, Dale, 157
mosquito, rain barrel, 20
moth (*Eophila fulicalis*), 33; black phase ("industrial moth"), 205–207,

*illus.*, 206; corn earworm, 207; cryptic (*Phigalia titea*), 205; silk (*Antheraea*), 79; *Stenoma algidelia*, 175; unnamed found near Oscalaria, Panama, 175–176
mound builder (magapode), 84
Mount Bruce Native Bird Reserve, New Zealand, 156
Mullen, David A,, 187
Mundt, Senator Karl, 204
Murie, Olaus, 89–90
Museum of Comparative Zoology, Cambridge, Massachusetts, 46
muskrat, 88
*Myxine glutinosa* (slime eel), 185–186

NASA, 5, 6
Nairobi National Park, Kenya, 117
*Nature, Journal of*, 4
Naval Oceanographic Office, 8
Nemertina (proboscis worm), 54
Newark, New Jersey Airport, 198–199
New York Zoological Society, 121
Nice, Margaret, 166–167
nutria (coyput), 205

octopus, 21, 24, 55, 182
*Oncorhynchus kisutch* (coho salmon), 202
opossum, 64–65, 70, 115, 180–181; tropical, 87
oriole, 168; Baltimore, 83
"os penis," 70
otter, sea, 87, *illus.*, 87; of Alaska, 137; of northern coast of California, 136–137, *illus.*, 137
owl, 125, 155; great grey, 19; barn, 155–156
Oxford, University of, 74, 150, 196
Oxford Forestry School, 196
oyster, 24, 70, 77; American, 54–55; European, 55

Paleocene, 48
paramecium, 49
parasitism, 108–110
parakeet, 85–86
Parasitological Institute, Hochst, Germany, 46
Paris Museum of Natural History, 14–15

parrot, African (*Agapornis*), 84–85, *illus.*, 85
*Passer domesticus domesticus* (house or English sparrow), 65, 73–74, 84, 205
*Parus caeruleus* (blue tit), 192–196
Payne, Roger, 11, 155–156
peacock, 18
Pederson, A., 107
penguins, 154–155; Adelie, 67; Humboldt, 154
pheasant, 65
*Phigalia titea* (cryptic moth), 205
Pierce, George W., 153
*Pisaster* (starfish of California coast), 130
plankton beds, 76–77
planula, 50
Platyhelminthe, 53
plover, Wilson's, 179–180
polyp (*Umbellulidae*), 8
porcupine, 71
porpoise, 44–45, 117
Port Authority of New York, 198
Poulter, T. C., 154–155
prairie dog, 89
proboscis worm (Nemertina), 54
Protista, 49
Protozoa, 49
Pye, J. D., 154

quail, bobwhite, 106, 204
Quay, William B., 187

rabbit, 72, 114, 123; cottontail, 87; white-sided jack, 180
rabbitfish, 182
rat, 191–192; cotton, 114
rattle snake, 35, 101, 152
red-eyed vireo, 169
*Reeves pheasant*, 17–18, *illus.*, 17
releaser, 150–151
reptiles, 60, 64; see also under individual name
research ship *Kane*, 8
Ribbands, C. R., 26
robin, 150–151, 169
Rockefeller Institute, 153
Rockefeller University, 11
Rocky Mountain Biological Station, 92–93

salmon, coho (*Oncorhynchus kisutch*), 202
sanddollars (Echinoderms), 30
San Francisco, University of, 187
San Francisco Zoological Society, 154
Sarcodine, 49
Sargent, T. D., 206
Sargasso fish, 175
Sargasso Sea, 61–62, 147
Savory, Dr. Theodore H., 74
sawfly, 3
Schenkel, Rudolf, 117–119
*Schistosoma mansohi* (fluke), 46–47
*Science, Journal of,* 4
scorpion, false, 74; water, 19
sea anemone, 9–10, *illus.*, 10, 50
sea cucumber, 183–184, *illus.*, 184
seahorse, 80
sea snake, 182
sea urchin (Echinoderm), 30–32, 182
seal, 70; fur, 154–155
Seregenti National Park, Tasmania, 139
sheep, bighorn, 43
shelduck, 107
shrew, 70–71, 115–116, *illus.*, 116
shrike, 133–134; loggerhead, 134; Northern, 133–134
shrimp, 158–159
sidewinder snake, 35
Singapore, University of, 138
Singapore Botanical Gardens, 138
sloth, 123; two-toed, 71
Smith, R. I., 73
snake, 35–37, 64, 152–153; see also under individual name
sniperscope camera, 155
songbird, "enemy," *illus.*, 149
Sonoran Desert, Arizona, 58, 163
Spallanzani, Lazaro, 153
sparrow, house or English (*Passer domesticus*), 65, 73–74, 84, 205; song, 166–167; tree, 73–74
spider, 34–35, 57–60; bola, 130–133, *illus.*, 131; crab (*Xysticus*), 59, *illus.*, 59; Gnaphoid, 58; jumping, 34; *Nephila*, 57; tarantula, 58
spiderling, 34
sponge, 24–25; bathtub, 24; sulphur, 24; red, 25, 52
spoonbill, 124

springtail, *illus.*, 29
squid, 21, 55–56, 177; black-hooded (*Vampyrotheuthis infernalis*), 177; *Thaumatolampas diadema*, 177–178
squirrel, 12–13, 115; fox, 88; tree, 70–71
starfish (*Echinoderm*), 30–32; *illus.*, 31, 130; of California coast (*Pisaster*), 130
star gazer, 182–183
starling, 167, 169, 197–198
Steinhart Aquarium, San Francisco, 45
*Stenoma algidella* (moth), 175
stickflea (*Echidnophaga gallinacea*), 130
sting ray, 182–183
"Studies in the Life History of the Song Sparrow" by Margaret Nice, 166
surgeonfish, 182
*susu* (blind dolphin), 45
swallow, 166; barn, 18, 169; wood, 19
swan, black-necked, 107, 108; black, 108
swift, 65; chimney, 81, 169; palm, 81–83, *illus.*, 82; tree, 81–84
Switzerland, University of, Department of Zoology, 117

tapeworm, 53–54, *illus.*, 53
tailor bird, 83–84
tanagers, 168
Taylor, Jan C., 12
tenrec (tenreecid), 71
tern, Alaskan, 168; Arctic, 167–168; fairy, 86
Teton National Park, 174
*Tetrahymena*, 49
*Thaumatolampas diadema* (squid), 177–178
thigmotaxis, 164–165
thrush, 168
tick, dog, 159–160
Tinbergen, Niko, 66, 111, 112
tit, blue (*Parus caeruleus*), 192–196
toad, 147; horned (western horned lizard), 189–190, *illus.*, 189
towhee, 180
turkey, 179
turtle, 103; box, 64; Galapagos, 134

*Umbellulidae* (polyps), 8
University College, London, 15
*Uroderma bilobatum* (bat of Panama), 88

*Vampyrotheuthis infernalis* (black-hooded squid), 77
Vera Falls, 93
viper, carpet, 37; jumping, 37; pit, 152
Virginia Institute of Marine Science, 9
*Volvox*, 51–52
von Frisch, Karl, 144
vulture, 139–140; Egyptian, 139–140, *illus.*, 139; hooded, 140; lappet-faced, 140; whitebacked, 140

warbler, 65; Kirkland's, 203
warthog, 118
wasp, 182
water bug (Belostomatidae), 125–126, *illus.*, 126
water moccasin, 101, 152
water ouzel, dipper, Cinclidae, 93–96; of American Rockies (*Cinclus mexicanus*), 93–96
water snake, 64, 101
weakfish, 160
weevil, leaf eating, 176–177, *illus.*, 176
Wenzel, Bernice M., 156–157
whale, 44–45; rorqual or fin-back, 44
whooping crane, 119–120, *illus.*, 120
wildebeestes, 118
Wildfowl Trust, England, 107
wolf, gray, 89–90; plains, 192
wombat, 64–65
woodduck, 107–108; white, 108–109
Woodin, Mr. William, 58
woodpecker, 18, 125
Woods Buffalo National Park, Saskatchewan, 120
Woods Hole Marine Biological Laboratory, Massachusetts, 25
wren, Carolina, 86

*Xiphophorus*, 61
X-ray, 157–158
*Xysticus* (crab spider), 59, *illus.*, 59

Young, J. Z., 15